Prehistoric Man
and the Primates

Other books by William E. Scheele

PREHISTORIC ANIMALS

THE FIRST MAMMALS

Prehistoric Man and the Primates

Written and illustrated by

WILLIAM E. SCHEELE

DIRECTOR, CLEVELAND MUSEUM OF NATURAL HISTORY

THE WORLD PUBLISHING COMPANY

CLEVELAND AND NEW YORK

PUBLISHED BY *The World Publishing Company*

2231 WEST 110TH STREET, CLEVELAND 2, OHIO

PUBLISHED SIMULTANEOUSLY IN CANADA BY

NELSON, FOSTER & SCOTT LTD.

Library of Congress Catalog Card Number: 57–7403

FIRST EDITION

CW

For

my mother and father

CONTENTS

All drawings of modern racial types on pps. 112–13, 115, 117
were done by Joann S. Scheele

Acknowledgments

I am most grateful to Miss Frances Bungart, Mrs. Alan Gerhardt, and most especially to my wife for help in assembling and typing this manuscript.

INTRODUCTION

VERY few subjects in nature claim as much public attention and interest as the story of man. The study of the races of mankind, or anthropology, takes many forms, and all of them must be considered together if they are to present a comprehensive story of the most unusual animal on earth, man. Paleoanthropology, the study of prehistoric and primitive human beings, also has a fascination for a great many people. Yet, unlike some other sciences, neither paleoanthropology nor anthropology offers the average individual much chance to participate personally as a collector or as an observer.

There are many reasons for this, but the principal ones are the shortage of truly ancient specimens and the fact that the few specimens which occasionally do turn up require highly specialized training to properly interpret their meanings. It is always true that an amateur collector can do valuable work in this or any science field, but the final study of racially important groups of people or their artifacts must remain in the hands of thoroughly trained individuals. So, while this subject of man is popular, it is also frustrating to the average person because the interrelated knowledge and experience needed to comprehend the related sciences are quite beyond most of us.

Most museums of natural history include displays that present an outline of mankind's evolution. Not all museums are large enough to include exhibits that go beyond this point, into the story of living races. However the subject may be presented, museum people have seen clearly the public's interest in knowing more about its origins.

Elementary school children are particularly fascinated by the story of the North American Indians and the cave men of Europe. High school and college students tend to be more interested in anatomy and are required to study the physical links between human animals and the other animals of the world. Adults looking at this kind of exhibit are very apt to want to know more specifically how human beings are related to the remainder of the animal world than the museum exhibits may tell them. They are interested in seeing point-by-point explanations for the conclusions recorded on labels and specimens.

This book does not attempt to tell the full story of anthropology; it is simply an effort to present graphically a sequence of available facts and specimens that anthropologists work with in acquainting their students and the public with the fascinating story of man's evolution. It indicates only the high points of this story, the more significant fragments of animal evolution that help link together the world of four-footed animals and the more recent development of human beings.

The animals that are illustrated or described here are primate mammals, the most highly developed order of animals. Nearly all of them have lived very recently or are still alive today. This book is a result of trying to present the story of the relationship of those animals which, science believes, are a link be-

6 feet

5 feet

4 feet

3 feet

2 feet

Gorilla   *Man*

Orangutan

Gibbon

Baboon

Old-world Monkey

New-world Monkey

Lemur

Tarsier

Tree Shrew

STATURE AND STRUCTURAL CHANGES HELP DEFINE THE PRIMATES

tween the earliest forms of pre-human animals and present-day races of human beings.

The book divides roughly into three sections. The first is a general descriptive résumé of certain vital aspects of anthropology and a brief review of the anatomy of human beings as it has a bearing upon anthropology. The second large section deals with the living primates of the world that are considered man's closest relatives in the animal kingdom. The third section begins with the oldest-known fossils of primates, and progresses quickly through geologic time sequences illustrating the important steps in evolution that helped primates evolve into human beings distinctive enough to warrant designation as a race.

The procession of animals in this section includes the earliest-known human beings and their best-known predecessors. A relatively few species of prehistoric man are described, for as the reader will see, only a few basic kinds of prehistoric men have been discovered to date.

The animals depicted in the volume were selected to strike a happy medium in agreement with the opinions of most of the important anthropologists working today. Arranging the animals in an acceptable and

proper order is a great problem, but where there is compromise, the compromise endeavors to reflect the opinion of several anthropologists.

The author only touches briefly on cultural anthropology; he describes primates in the broadest terms possible, and has made no attempt to divide the races of men into any group more complex than racial subdivisions. He has simply tried to trace man's progress as an animal from the earliest division of basic human stock into its major evolutionary lines to the point at which man becomes what we call civilized.

Prehistoric Man and the Primates is the final part of a series of three books by the author. The first, *Prehistoric Animals,* surveyed animal life in our world from a time more than 500 million years ago through the dinosaur dominance of the world. *The First Mammals* described prehistoric mammals of the world who lived until the time man began to assume dominance of the living animals on earth. This third and final volume, then, is the story of the beginnings of man and the path human evolution is thought to have followed in reaching modern man's advanced state of technological progress.

PRIMATES AND MAN

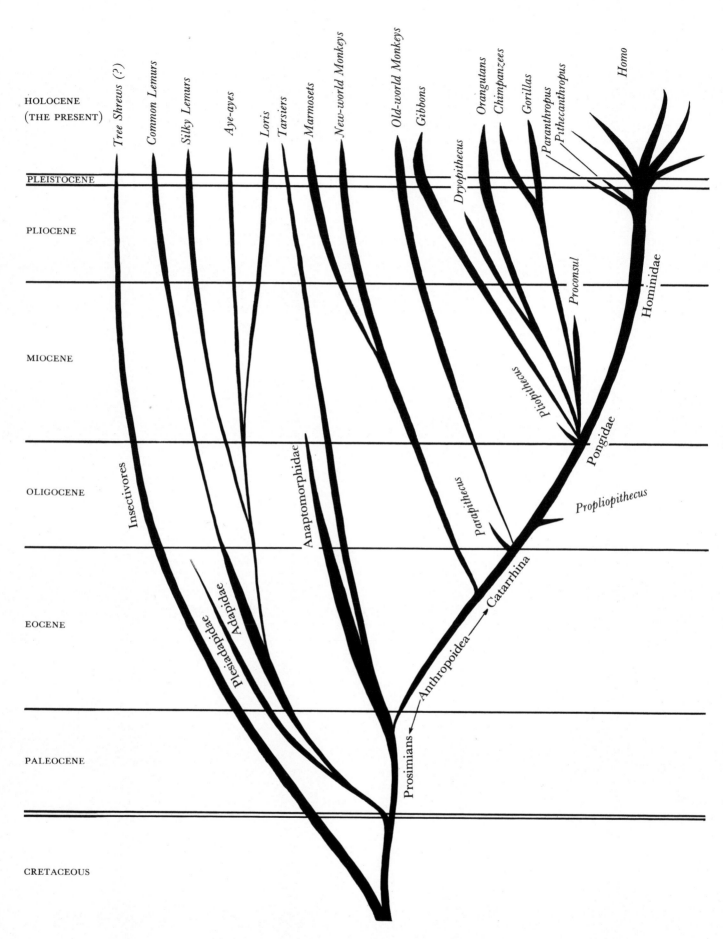

CHART OF THE RELATIONSHIPS OF PRIMATE MAMMALS

WHEN THE great scientist Linnaeus was struggling with the monumental task of classifying the animals of the world, he carefully chose the word primate to designate the order of mammals that includes lemurs, monkeys, apes, and man. The word means "one who is first in rank or quality," and in the opinion of many taxonomists who have followed Linnaeus, the name was well chosen.

Those who enjoy knowing facts about the biological sciences are familiar with the Linnaean classification of animals that places man and the anthropoid apes in a niche above all other animal forms. But a visit to a zoo will clearly illustrate the gap that separates the alert apelike creatures and all of the so-called lower forms of animal life. The gap that separates these animals is biologically a big one; the differences between apes and man are, in turn, equally big. But all of these "top mammals" share enough physical features to be grouped together as primates.

Anthropologists, paleontologists, and others working in related sciences have long felt that the earth will eventually yield enough fossils to tell us the full story of what took place to bridge the gap between the apes and man, and that the evidence will fall into a sequence that cannot be disputed. At present, even without such step-by-step fossil evidence, those working in these sciences feel able to describe man's lineage or to predict man's future. There are just enough bony remains available now to provide a bare outline of man's evolution, but these men are encouraged by past experience which has often proven them right.

Many times in the past, biologists have described unknown intermediate animal forms which were needed to link separate parts of the animal kingdom and which, they stated, ought to be present in the fossil record. And many times over, such forms have turned up after long searching.

The Bodies of Apes and Man Are Unique
in Five Major Ways

To UNDERSTAND why man is placed among the mammals called primates, it is necessary to reflect upon the uniqueness of his body, and to compare it with anatomical features found in other primates.

FIRST FEATURE

Among all primates, one of the most outstanding characteristics is the fact that the hands are grasping, or prehensile. This adaptation is directly related to the prehistory of the entire order, to a time in the distant past when the first pre-primate mammals began to climb trees and thereby set themselves apart from other ground and water-dwelling mammals.

Cats, squirrels, and other animals less specialized than primates climb trees by digging into the bark with their sharp claws. Primates do not have claws; they progress through branches and along the trunks of trees by grasping with their thumbs and fingers. The ability to place the thumb in what is called opposition to the fingers is also necessary to perform delicate movements of the hands. Eventually this faculty made possible modern man's supreme mechanical abilities.

The primate's ability to rotate the lower arm freely at the elbow and to move its arm freely at the shoulder is also very important. This characteristic in the primates is aided and made possible by the presence of the clavicle, or collarbone. The clavicle acts as a prop to hold the shoulder joint steady. This unique bone allows monkeys to climb and swing through trees, and it allows man to do

such unusual things as pitch a baseball, or chin on an iron bar, or to do anything else that depends upon freedom of arm movement.

What may seem like an insignificant difference between primates and other mammals is the presence of toenails rather than claws. Flat nails are vital to an animal who grasps and manipulates objects. Claws would be a nuisance. Some of the lower primates retain one or more digits that bear a specialized claw; these perform a limited function. But in man and the great apes, the nails are flat and broad. In this respect they are unique in the animal world. The uniqueness of the primate's ability to grasp objects firmly is emphasized by the ridges and pads on its fingers that produce fingerprints; these are a further refinement of the ability to grip things.

SECOND FEATURE

The primate has the ability to walk and to stand erect, freeing arms and hands for other activities. To accomplish this, the foot of a man has developed far differently from the grasping feet of other primates. Anatomists tell us that examination of the structural detail of the human foot reveals a relationship to an earlier, grasping stage, although it is not possible to see that man's great toe was ever able to function as the thumb does on the hand.

THIRD FEATURE

The brain of primates is unusual because of its large size in relation to the total body weight, and the complexity of its outer surface. Folds and creases in the brain's outer surface are directly related to the nervous activity of the animal. Among man and apes, this surface is highly complex. Some primates have simpler brains than others, but man's brain, compared to the brain of all other mammals, is a super development. It is apparently still evolving toward a more complex state of organization.

MAN'S GREAT GIFTS HELPED HIM ACHIEVE
HIS UNIQUE PLACE AMONG THE MAMMALS

Forward-looking eyes

Stereoscopic vision

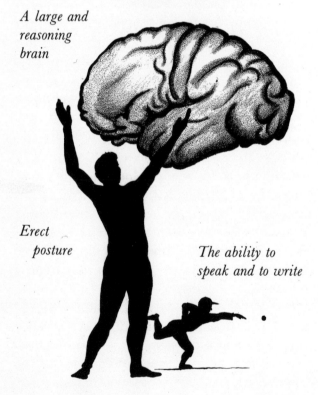

*A large and
reasoning
brain*

*Erect
posture*

*The ability to
speak and to write*

*Rotating lower arm and
opposable thumb and fingers*

MONKEYS SHARE THESE
IMPORTANT GIFTS WITH MAN

*Forward-looking eyes
Stereoscopic vision*

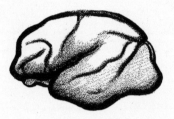

*A large brain in proportion
to the body*

*Erect posture
(limited)*

*Grasping fingers,
opposable thumb, and rotating
lower arm*

*Ability to communicate with
sounds (limited)*

FOURTH FEATURE

The eyes of primates are unusual because they provide keen stereoscopic vision. The skull has a unique socket for the eye which completely seals off the eyeball from the remainder of the head. The ability to identify objects at a distance from the eye is an asset

17

of incomparable value to animals as defensively helpless as man. In nearly all of the primates the sense of smell is much reduced; this is also true of man. The loss of the ability to smell well is apparently related to the dependence upon good eyesight for protection and the ability to hunt.

FIFTH FEATURE

Perhaps the most unique gift of all belongs to man alone. It is his power of speech—the ability to record and to pass along to others the accumulated knowledge of centuries.

These few obvious anatomical features are evidence enough to the scientist to set primates completely apart from all other mammals. Apes share these unusual gifts with man to some extent, but the reasoning brain has led to culture and enables man to use his physical gifts in ways that other animals cannot.

Human beings and other primates share the same general reproductive habits, too. With relatively few exceptions, primates bear but one living young at a time, and the female nurses this youngster for a long time. The rate of growth to maturity in young primates is slower than that in any other animal. There is considerable dependence of the young upon the adults—for more than a year in some apes and monkeys, for many years in the case of man. The female usually has two nursing breasts, and these are placed high on the body, differing considerably from the abdominal position of the breasts of most other mammals. The long childhood and perpetual learning ability of human beings is a poorly understood but important asset to man.

The Biological Classification of Man

By COMPARING primates to all other animals as a taxonomist (the man who classifies things) might, we arrive at a clearer idea of how their anatomy places them in the top rank over all other mammals.

Our world is broadly split into three major divisions called kingdoms. The first and largest division is the mineral kingdom. Growing in and on top of that we find the plant kingdom, and directly dependent upon both of these is the animal kingdom. Obviously man belongs in this latter group.

Next, there is a subkingdom of the animal kingdom called the Metazoa. This category recognizes the fact that our bodies are made up of many varied kinds of cells. Man's great size places him in this subkingdom.

Man's complex system of nerves that makes up the spinal column and helps hold him erect, places him in the phylum Chordata. Because the spinal column consists of individual small bones, the subphylum Vertebrata further distinguishes him.

There are four classes of animals; primates, because they are warm-blooded and have hair and other typically mammalian features, are placed in the class Mammalia. Further division into the subclass Eutheria accents the development of the young mammals inside of the mother, within a sac, to be born in an advanced stage of growth.

The next biological subdivision divides these Eutherian mammals into nine orders. Observing the hands, the use of the arms, keen vision, complex brain, and other unique structures, a biologist classifying man would be forced to conclude that monkeys, apes, and men belong together as superior animals. They are therefore placed in the ninth and highest order, called Primates.

ESKIMO (MONGOLOID)

BERBER (WHITE)

FOREST NEGRO

Lemurs, tarsiers, and their relatives are included within this order, but not all primates are equally specialized. To recognize levels of difference, suborders within the order are created. Anthropoidea is the name of the suborder in which man is placed with the monkeys and apes.

Comparing feet, face, posture, and the like with those of other anthropoids, the classifier next decides that men are quite distinctive from the apes, and must be grouped as a separate family. This family is called the Hominidae.

Within this family the genus *Homo* describes many fossil as well as living men. The species name *sapiens,* meaning "thinking," describes the final zoological division. Those men who could reason have survived as the most numerous large animal on earth.

From this point, biology and culture interact to create problems, for some groups of modern people are not content to be defined as *Homo sapiens* alone. Vanity demands further subdivision of the species. The most casual glance at the variations between living human beings quickly separates those persons with light skins into a Caucasoid stock, individuals with yellow skin characteristics into a Mongoloid stock, and those with dark skin traits into a Negroid stock. But even these basic divisions are far more difficult to trace than they appear to be at first glance.

In a zoological sense, the differences that separate the stocks are small, and it is even smaller anatomical differences plus outside environmental factors that further divide the three basic stocks into races. In this modern day, it is virtually impossible to find what could be called a pure race. Modern intergroup communications have made possible every conceivable variation in human genetics, and these differences are so subtle that they make any further classification of man impossible. It is important to remember that religions, speech differences, or geographic boundaries do not create a race.

In abbreviated form, man's status within the modern system of animal classification would look like this:

Kingdom	Animal	
Subkingdom	Metazoa	
Phylum	Chordata	
Subphylum	Vertebrata	
Class	Mammalia	
Subclass	Eutheria	
Order	Primate	
Suborder	Anthropoidea	
Family	Hominidae	
Genus Homo		
Species Sapiens	Caucasoid stock Mongoloid stock Negroid stock	

It is difficult for some people to be objective about man as he is related to other animals. There is no surer way of beginning an argument than to discuss the ancestry of man. It is a difficult subject to present in public museums and is hard to clarify in a science curriculum that endeavors to teach basic scientific fact. Many people willingly concede the biological classification of all other animals in the world and yet find it difficult to grasp what science agrees is a proper definition of man himself. Mankind's total age and modern man's relationship to living primates are often disputed.

Anthropology Is Needed To Help Us Understand Ourselves

THERE IS something in the make-up of many people that does not permit them to think of human beings as animals, just as it is difficult for some people to believe that our earth's surface is in a constantly changing state. To escape comparing man to the other animals, early biologists went so far as to develop systems of animal classification setting man on a plane by himself, free from comparison with other animals. In contrast, modern anthropology seeks to understand man by comparing him in utmost detail to other animals. Anthropology has, in fact, become so complex that it is difficult to explain exactly how many things are considered in attempting to evaluate man properly. To help this situation, anthropology has been divided into two major divisions. That part of it concerned with man's appearance, his internal organs, and his general structure is physical anthropology. The tools men use, the things man does as an individual and in groups, the dwellings he uses, and other things of that sort

are part of cultural anthropology. Man is the only animal capable of forming and maintaining a culture, but the growth of any culture rests upon a foundation of biology. This book only touches briefly on aspects of cultural anthropology.

This science that studies man had its modern beginnings approximately one hundred years ago. The first museum specifically established to study man and man's relationship to other animals was founded in Germany in 1886. From the beginning, men who chose to enter this field of scientific experience were men of varied backgrounds; some were lawyers, some were doctors or businessmen; this variety reflects the interest in men's backgrounds that is present in every level of our modern society. People want to know more about other people, those alive and those of the past.

In our own country, anthropology was first introduced into a college curriculum in 1885 —at Harvard. The first doctor's degree in the science was awarded in 1892 at Clark University. But nothing has had such an explosive impact on any new science as the publication of Charles Darwin's *The Origin of Species* in 1859. From that time until today, reports of new progress in the study of man's origins have been sure-fire news stories, and "man the curious" reveals one of his basic primate traits in being curious about his intriguing background.

Early anthropologists had a common goal; they realized that to appreciate man's past and learn anything at all about what might happen to us in the future, the facts of man's development had to be presented without emotion. As fossil hunters began to provide the bones on which to base the story of early man, it became evident that the history could not be told without conflict. Bones of extinct man-apes can be dated as far back as 1,500,-000 years, yet it is only within the last 500,000 years that evidence of man's cultural progress can be seen. Such knowledge presents a problem, for some people will not accept as fact anything that appears to challenge their notion that "the animals" originate in a stock inferior to man.

During the last fifty years, Darwin's work has been absorbed into our total biological knowledge, and it is no longer necessary to argue scientific-versus-Biblical interpretation of man's origins. If accepted nonliterally, religious writings are a poetic tracing of many colossal events in the origin and evolution of all life on earth. These descriptions anticipated modern science in many ways and are a beautifully written interpretation of a complex subject.

Fossils of Man Are Rare

FOSSILS ARE readily accepted as evidence of extinct life and are well understood by many people, but only a very few people understand what a minute fraction of all living things from the past are *ever* found in fossil form. Though the remains of literally millions of water-dwelling animals are found, they represent only a small part of the total number that once lived. Fossils of plants and of some kinds of mammals are very well known, but these, too, are represented by thousands rather than millions of fossils. Two specialized kinds of animals are seldom found as fossils. Bird remains are scarce, and the collected bones of very ancient human beings can be counted on the fingers on one's hands. These two are the rarest of all fossils.

Extinct birds are rare because their bones were hollow and thus easily destroyed. Birds were also quick enough to escape the colossal catastrophes in nature that produce numerous fossils. The remains of ancient men are far more rare than those of birds; man's living habits have apparently always been such that he too was able to escape most disasters.

In relation to the age of the earth, even the oldest men lived so recently that their re-

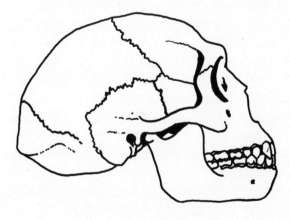

SKULL OF PEKING MAN

mains are very close to the surface of the earth and thus subject to disintegration by weather and disturbances of the surface soil. Floods and landslides, in particular, have been responsible for the shifting or destruction of many important deposits. Another point to remember is that the world's human population was not very large until recent times.

Fragments from the skeletons of prehistoric human beings have been found in sand and gravels deposited by water, and many remains, buried under the thin dust layers of centuries, are found in caves. Still others found in caves were buried by landslides. Volcanoes have caused the sudden death of entire animal populations, and a few rare human specimens have been taken from the sterile water of ice-age bogs.

There is some evidence that prehistoric humans were cannibals, and if so, they would have been partly responsible for the scarcity of their own contemporaries. Skulls were sometimes collected as trophies; in some instances, apparently skulls were broken so that the brains could be eaten, and the empty skull was used as a cup. One wonders what happened to the remainder of these skeletons. Were the bodies left to decompose, or were they eaten by the captors? Primitive men have always smashed open the bones of their prey in order to eat the marrow. Some sites have yielded splinters of human bone that might have been splintered for that same purpose.

In almost every instance in which science is dealing with really significant human bones, the pitifully small amount of bone

available from a single specimen is a most distressing factor. The finest fossils known to science are those created when animal remains were quickly smothered before decay and scavengers destroyed the evidence of the dead bodies. Even the earliest men were very alert animals and usually escaped such fateful events.

North American anthropologists desiring to study ancient men have no really old specimens from this continent, Central, or South America to work with. The oldest evidence we have of man's presence within the United States dates from approximately 30,000 years ago. All of the better-known specimens of a more ancient man collected to date come from Africa, Europe, and Asia, and these are among the most precious properties of the world's great museums. In our own country, plaster casts of original bone are all that are available to help us understand man's earliest background. In this country, there are no more than thirty men and women actively working in the field of physical anthropology. This low figure reflects to some extent the scarcity of study material from the recent past as well as from the distant past.

The science of anthropology is in part a study of anatomical details, and in the relatively short time since it has developed, many systems for measuring and plotting the growth patterns and structure of individuals and races have been devised. To the average reader, some of the details studied and described by anthropologists appear too minor or irrelevant to have a bearing on man's story. But all known living men are a single species of animal; it is only the minor differences that separate races or subspecies.

Detailed comparison of the body and skeleton of man with that of the higher apes shows incredible structural similarities that are not always evident on the surface. Muscle for muscle and bone for bone such a comparison offers plentiful evidence supporting the theory that apes and men developed from a common stock, that they did so quite separately, and that the separation from that stock was made many millions of years ago. How this occurred is not readily seen in available fossil evidence.

No reputable scientist has ever tried to say that modern men are a sudden offshoot of a union between monkeys. When Charles Darwin indicated a possible common origin of men and other primates, he was not basing his opinion upon actual fossil specimens of bone. He was doing what every scientist of his time was forced to do—judging animal relationship by the outward appearances and the structural plan of living animal bodies available for study. Paleontology has since supplied the evidence to support nearly all major evolutionary theories, but the case for man's progress through time is still doubted by some people, primarily because remains of extinct human beings are extremely scarce.

Since old human bones are so rare, each piece that comes to light is classified slowly, and complete understanding of its implications requires the most skillful doctor's knowledge of anatomy. Teamwork of the closest kind is necessary to remove important finds in the field. The digging team, the geologist, and everyone connected with the appraisal of important specimens must work with great care to avoid any possibility of error.

Dating remains of ancient human beings is difficult because the geology of the ice age and the centuries that followed the glaciers presents a special problem of mixed soil layers so near the surface that even present-day rivers and floods can upset the sequence of those layers. The most careful observations are required to determine how a bone might have been deposited. Its chemical content is tested, careful graphs are made to show the profile of the surrounding soil, and of course any animal remains found with human bones are fully identified in an effort to fit all parts of any find into its proper geologic horizon.

The first fossils of mammals to be excavated in great numbers came out of rocks much older than those of the ice age. The large number of the new discoveries and the clear story they told made it possible to illustrate many of the processes of mammal evolution. The story of man's evolution through time is still not as complete as that of most other mammals.

It was not until 1891 that the first really important find of a prehistoric man was made; it came from the remote island of Java. Of course, other remains had already been

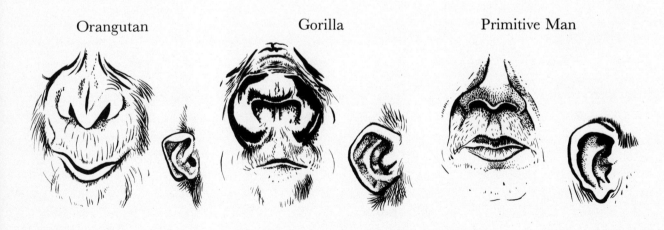

Orangutan   Gorilla   Primitive Man

COMPARISON OF NOSES AND EARS

found in Europe, but most of these were given little attention; they were brushed aside as abnormalities or assumed to be the remains of big apes. Sometimes, they looked too much like modern remains to gain serious attention.

The bitter arguments that arose over the identity of the first finds of early man helped stimulate more expeditions and closer scrutiny of everything that was turned up that could possibly fill out man's story. Old finds were critically reviewed. Discoveries made in Europe and then in the Far East were tantalizing because they showed just enough physical evidence of the antiquity of man to erase any doubts in the minds of anthropologists that primates and men were structurally similar although not closely related.

In the 1920's rich South African deposits produced important discoveries that traced the line of primate development back still further. They revealed evidence of animals with apelike brains and faces whose nearly erect posture left the hands and arms free for near-human uses.

About this time, too, scientists realized that it would have been impossible for men to have derived from monkeys, simply because man's body is too unspecialized to enable him to act and live like a monkey. Man's body size was too great to permit tree dwelling, human teeth had become generalized in pattern and structure, human hands and feet were not suited by nature to a monkey's tree-dwelling habits. Nature's adaptation of man's bones and muscles had forced him into an earth-bound existence.

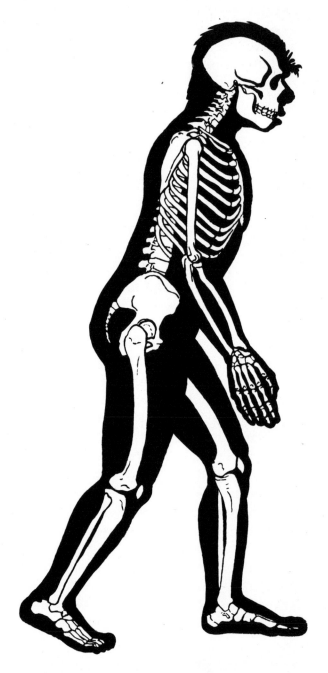

SKELETON OF NEANDERTHAL MAN

The Importance of Statistics and Laboratory Experiments

TODAY'S RESEARCH in anthropology takes as many forms as research does in any modern science.

Some of the methods that have been developed to describe variations among human beings have had their inspiration in practical

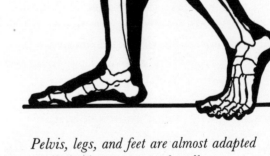

problems, most of which have dealt with measurements of the human body. The assembly of these statistics has enabled physical anthropologists to go forward at a rapid pace when the opportunities for compiling statistics about great masses of people have been good.

The statistics gathered by the military services during recent conflicts throughout the world are the best example of this kind of research. The armed forces, out of need for a definite set of standards to govern the manufacture of clothing and other things which would have wide use, found it necessary to tabulate accurately many diverse sets of measurements needed to answer questions about the average dimensions of people. These statistics were eventually made available to anthropologists who have, in turn, been able to use them to advance some of their own theories, or to make further researches about the outside factors that produce differences in our body shape and total structure.

After basic statistics were analyzed, laboratory experiments were necessary to prove certain doubtful points. Repeatedly it was confirmed that bones themselves do not assume their typical shapes independently of other factors. The stress of muscles and other body growth factors can materially alter the size and shape of bones.

As the anatomist sees it, man's ribs, arms, hands, and the larger bones that comprise the main portion of the spine, including the shoulder blades, were the first parts of the human skeletal framework to evolve to their present condition. This assumption seems reasonable when we make a simple comparison

*Pelvis, legs, and feet are almost adapted
to our distinctive posture and walk*

SKELETON OF MODERN MAN

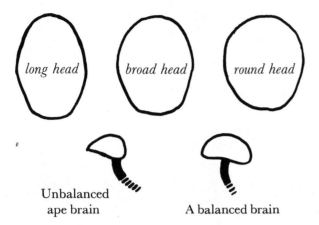

long head   broad head   round head

Unbalanced
ape brain   A balanced brain

of this section of our skeleton with that of almost any other similar mammal, notably the apes and monkeys.

The second large area of our body to evolve into its present form was that which includes the pelvis, our legs, and feet. This contention seems to be borne out by the fossil remains of apelike animals in which the bones of the leg were beginning to show modification for erect walking many millions of years before the first men appeared. Many doctors believe that this lower area of our body is still evolving, and they cite the numerous troubles human beings have with their joints, and bones of the legs, feet, and lower back as proof of the fact. The stresses that produce deformities and pain in later years of life seem to be due to one of the oldest and most basic problems of our body— adjusting to an erect posture and a two-legged walking habit.

The final body unit to evolve into its present form was the head and its contents, and the first bone of the spinal column—the atlas. The face, the brain, and the teeth apparently assumed their modern form only recently, although there have been no noticeable changes in these three areas of the body since the time of the Cro-Magnon cave dwellers.

Many anatomists believe that even today, our teeth, the complex development of our brain, and to some extent the shape of our face are still undergoing very slight, but dimly

26

traceable changes. The extreme variability of human teeth is cited as a prime example of this.

The opening in the base of the skull that admits the spinal cord and all of its nerve impulses from the body is also thought to be modifying. Some feel that the placement of the brain on the spinal cord and the over-all shape of the brain have been slowly modifying for many millions of years. These men believe that the spinal cord will someday lead more directly into the center of the brain and thus give it a more perfect balance. In the meantime, the total brain shape may alter from its present oval shape to a nearly perfect circular cap. The human being's erect posture will continue to adjust slightly, and the head will balance on the spinal column more comfortably than it does today. How long such changes may take is a doubtful thing to predict.

Men in all branches of science must continue to amass tremendous collections of skeletons and body parts as well as statistics about human beings. The need for such museum collections is not always evident. By the same token, the need for specific data cannot always be predicted, but time and again re-

APACHE INDIAN

search has found leads to answers in the massed materials and data of those who had the instinct and foresight to collect and tabulate. Big skeletal collections are a luxury to an institution, yet they are the basis for much elemental research.

The constitution of individual people and of entire racial groups of human beings has been linked with traits of behavior. As the human population of the world increases by tremendous numbers every year, the effects of outside factors on the total development of the human body will assume new meanings; the complete understanding of these meanings will be important to the well-being of the entire world. It is quite possible that anthropologists can help avert a great many troubles created by men who fail to see clearly the consequences of mixing racial types, of shifting village or island populations, of mass diet changes, and similar acts that have disastrous effects upon the individuals involved.

Teeth and Tooth Rows

SINCE SO MANY known fossil forms of primates consist of teeth and jaws it is important to examine the over-all tooth patterns of these animals to see how they differ in appearance from those of human beings.

The size and biting surface of the molars in apes and humans are particularly distinctive. The huge canine teeth present in the apelike forms are absent in human beings. Most distinctive of all is the over-all shape of the tooth row in the upper and lower jaws. In human beings the continuous row of teeth has a rounded appearance, and there are no gaps between any of the teeth. In apes the tooth rows run in two parallel lines with a more sharply rounded forward section. In the apes there is a gap between the incisors and the canine teeth, and there is a distinctive shelf of bone, called the simian shelf, in the lower jaw. This is never present in human beings.

Since teeth are the most durable part of any skeleton, they have received intensive study by research scientists. The average person may scoff at the deductions made on the basis of a few teeth, but that is only because he has no conception of the amount of information that can be derived from the internal structure, the biting surface, and external appear-

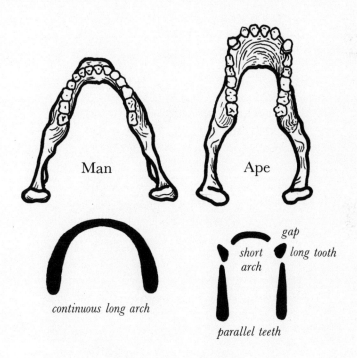

continuous long arch

short arch *gap* *long tooth*

parallel teeth

TOOTH ROWS IN THE LOWER JAW

ance of a single tooth. Teeth are the most distinctive structures a paleontologist can work with.

The density of the bones of the jaws is an important aid to their preservation, and these bones have also received their share of detailed study. The presence of a chin in human beings is poorly understood but is none the

27

less a significant feature of human anatomy. The projection of the front teeth in apelike forms and the lack of chin are distinctive points that help separate early and modern human beings from the closely related apes.

Piltdown man, now known as the Piltdown hoax, was long considered important to the story of human evolution because of the primitive chinless lower jaw in a modern-looking skull. Such an intermediate human head form with no chin would have conveniently rounded out part of the human evolution story. The depth and size of the lower jaw plus the tooth pattern were too good to be true.

The Piltdown story should be told, however, for it carries several valuable lessons. Too much museum protection was given the original bone; it was not readily available for detailed scrutiny and testing until recently. Reporters of the disclosure generally fail to

THE FACES OF APES AND MAN COMPARED

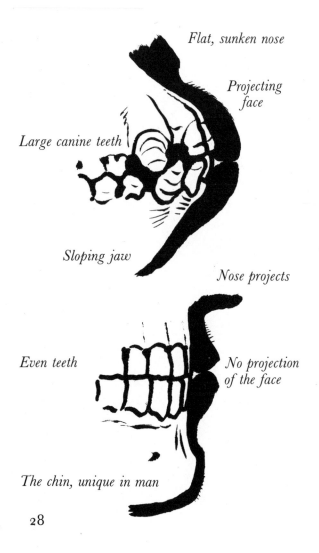

Flat, sunken nose

Projecting face

Large canine teeth

Sloping jaw

Nose projects

Even teeth

No projection of the face

The chin, unique in man

28

The simian gap

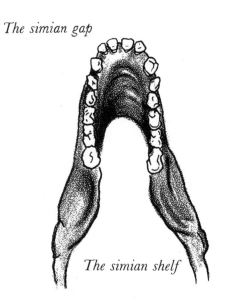

The simian shelf

point out that many scientists who had originally ventured opinions on these bones many years ago were basing their opinions on imperfect plaster casts from the original bones. There were also no real attempts on the part of the reporters to make it clear that many of the most careful men in the field of anthropology had always regarded the discovery as a questionable association of specimens.

The declaration that Piltdown man (in reality, a female skull) was a missing link had always been largely the work of the news writers' desire to capitalize on the public's fascination for our earliest ancestors. These same news sources were loudest and quickest to criticize the British Museum and scientists in general after the British Museum freely admitted the basic error of identification. Excellent and important work of the museum's own staff remedied this mistaken opinion; the laboratory detective work that revealed the hoax was in itself worthy of far more recognition than it has ever received. It is unfortunate that a news story like that of the Piltdown hoax casts doubt upon the validity of all scientific discoveries about the prehistory of humans.

As one result of all this, anthropologists, archaeologists, geologists, and others who must, from time to time, make public statements about their work have become overly cautious of what they say. Too often their words have been poorly understood or improperly reported. When scientists make a new discovery, they are apt to take an unduly long time to publish their opinions because they want to be certain that there is no chance for error. They are apt to be so cautious in reporting that it is hard for the general reader to attach sufficient importance to the conclusions they may print. Each year sees new evidence turned up to fill out the story of our predecessors. Much of the newly found material must wait for evaluation until extensive additional excavating can be finished and the time found to write full descriptions.

Finding Names for New Discoveries

ANTHROPOLOGY often suffers because some of the people who find important bones are sometimes unwilling to yield minor points in order to classify their new specimens with previously described similar remains. There is a marked tendency among even the best descriptive anatomists to feel that the material they work with personally is distinctive enough to warrant separate classifications. As a result, practically every discovery of fossil human beings bears a new name, and it usually has a popular local name and a locality name as well. These names may or may not accurately reflect a structural difference deserving of separation from other well-known species or subspecies.

Since the very earliest discoveries of fossil remains of human beings, it has been traditional to give the specimen to be described a common name based upon the geographic locality from which it was taken. For example, Neanderthal man is named for the famous Neanderthal valley near Düsseldorf in Germany; the Mount Carmel skeletons were found in caves on the slopes of Mount Carmel in what was then Palestine.

Many well-known finds have a bearing on the story of the Neanderthal people. Here is a list of some of them, giving the site name that has been assigned each specimen. This partial list will serve as an example of the way discoveries could be related by a more simple classification of similar specimens.

A NEANDERTHAL MIXTURE

Country	Locality	Popular Name	Date	Race
Belgium	Namur	Spy	1886	
France	Corrèze	La Chapelle aux-Saints	1908	ALL ARE
	Dordogne	Le Moustier	1908	BASICALLY
Germany	Düsseldorf	Neanderthal	1856	NEANDER-
	Württemberg	Steinheim	1933	THALS
Palestine	Mount Carmel	Mount Carmel	1931–32	
Italy	Rome	Monte Circeo	1935	

A constant problem that needs explanation is the fact that European discoveries and localities bear names that are virtually unknown to American readers, and thus are confusing. The reason for this is obvious—the glacial and interglacial periods as they are plotted in Europe bear names that are distinctive to that continent; they do not coincide with names applied to the same general movements of glacial ice on this continent.

Missing Links

THERE HAS always been considerable talk about missing links, much of it stemming from the belief that scientists are continually seeking rare remains of animals that will give them the key to understanding all of nature. People are particularly willing to believe that the story of man's evolution can be made complete by one lucky find. There is no single missing link, but there are many small gaps in the story of man's evolution. The biggest one spans a period of about twenty million years in the very earliest part of man's development.

The forces of nature that ended the 150-million-year reign of the reptiles on earth seems to have cleared the way for the spread of early mammal populations and continual experimentation within their forms. The puzzle lies in knowing which mammals were already well established while the dinosaurs still lived, and we will not know the answer until Cretaceous and Paleocene rocks containing numerous mammalian fossils of the right kind are discovered.

In size and general appearance, the oldest mammals known to us are already too modern-looking to have come into being without a long ancestry. That ancestry is poorly understood and, similarly, it is the earliest prehistory of man himself that is the least-known part of his story.

The discovery of the remains of a lemur some years ago in Eocene rocks of North America jolted paleontologists. Prior to this find it was assumed that primates were a very recent kind of animal; perhaps they evolved quickly just prior to the ice age. But finding a reasonably modern-looking lemur that is sixty million years old raises the probability that even the primates were well established at the time the ruling reptiles were becoming extinct.

The remains of fish, amphibians, reptiles, and certain mammals that link together important stages of animal development have been found. From them, we can deduce the evolution of animals from a watery habitat to a warm-blooded and active life over all of the

NOTHARCTUS, A FOSSIL LEMUR FROM NORTH AMERICAN DEPOSITS

earth's surface. Enough of man's evolution is known from fossils so that the links which are missing are not essential to prove his evolution. It is the bones that will indicate the path man followed in spreading over all the continents of the world that are still missing. These would give us the clues to a most interesting part of man's story.

Is There Another Species of Human Beings
in Our World?

FOOTPRINTS of two distinctly different early human types have been found in the hardened mud of European caves. One of these is the print of the Neanderthal man; the other is the clear print of a Cro-Magnon man. These footprints show what we might expect to find: the Neanderthal type had a broad stubby-looking foot that was flattened and crude; the foot of the Cro-Magnon man, who is considered essentially modern, does indeed look like the footprint of a present-day person.

These prints are interesting because some people have long thought that there may be hidden away in the Himalayas a second kind of living human being, the creature they call the "abominable snowman." Men of scientific repute have seen tracks of this snowman, and one has made a drawing that is shown alongside the footprints of earlier man and modern

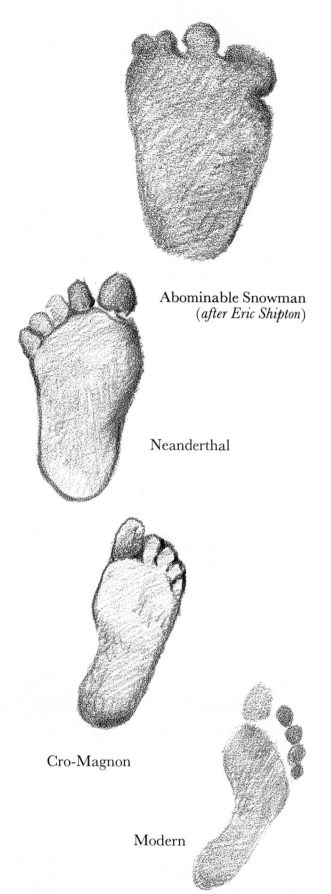

Abominable Snowman
(*after Eric Shipton*)

Neanderthal

Cro-Magnon

Modern

man. It has often been suggested that this snowman is in reality a survivor of the crude Neanderthal race.

Other scientists who have studied this problem tell us that the track could be that of a snow leopard or a similar mountain animal. The print when found is usually aged, and in the process broadened to the point where it looks to be of near-human size. Tracks made in the snow are difficult to interpret. One must be an expert to decide how old such tracks are, and to what degree they have been altered by the melting of the snow's surface. This is the argument advanced by those who favor the snow leopard as the creator of the snowman's tracks. These men also point to the inhospitable climate and altitude—a major barrier to human survival in those mountains.

A Single Species

LOOKING AT MAN as science would classify any animal, it is clear that all races of modern men are variations of a single species—*Homo sapiens*. This is a difficult statement for many people to accept as fact, for some people tend to see only the obvious surface variations which differentiate them from their neighbors. To them, these surface variations are important differences.

On the other hand, most people fail to see the very obvious *similarities* among men.

The best of anatomists working with skeletal material alone cannot tell races of man apart with certainty. Careful observation of an entire body would be necessary to properly separate humans into their commonly accepted racial divisions. This is not surprising, for paleontologists working with the bones of horses and zebras are unable to tell us that the zebra wears stripes. Similarly, a camel skeleton does not reveal that the camel has a hump, nor that the Asiatic camel differs from the North African species by having two humps.

Using skeletal remains alone, then, to determine differences between ancient men, we can observe at least three basic stages, known to us through his bones, in man's development. The first of these is the voluminous series of skeletal finds from South Africa which represent manlike apes of small stature that are grouped together and called Australopithecines. This word, meaning "southern apes," is a deceiving name, for most readers assume that the animals were discovered or were somehow linked to Australia. From the available bones known and described, it is clear that these primates stood very nearly erect and had begun to hunt, anticipating what we consider early human traits. The brain and facial character appear to have been apelike, but in the teeth, leg bones, and certain other parts there is a definite step forward in the evolutionary processes from pure ape characters. South Africa has provided some of the most thrilling recent discoveries in the field of paleoanthropology. The problem has been to have the finds described quickly so that the skeletons can be properly interpreted in relation to other ancient finds from that same region.

PILTDOWN MAN

Once a convenient jaw type, now nothing but a good lesson

The second large group of bones important to human evolution is typified by remains of the erect ape-man from Java. A closely related form has since been found on the mainland of Asia near Peking. In this more nearly modern human being, the size of the brain has increased. There must have been a more

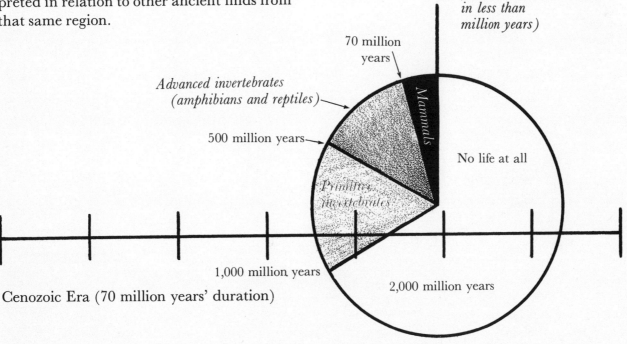

THE BEGINNINGS OF MAN IN RELATION TO THE OTHER DOMINANT LIFE ON EARTH

Man

*Very large
brain case*

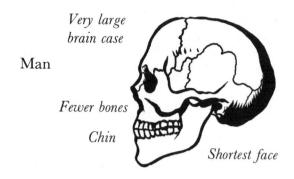

Fewer bones

Chin

Shortest face

Lemur

Shorter face

Mammallike reptile

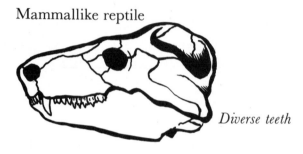

Diverse teeth

Reptile

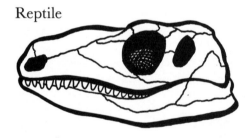

Amphibian

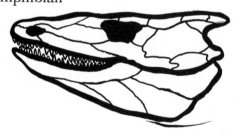

Bony fish

Jaws of cartilage

 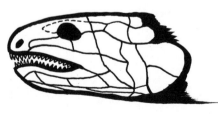

Shark

Many bones

near-human look to the face, and the leg bones—what few have been found—are straight, indicating that this man had achieved an almost fully erect walking posture.

From this point in the history of the earliest humans to a modern human type there is a gap in the evidence that cannot be presently filled.

The third and best-known stage in human evolution is best typified by the Cro-Magnon man and the Neanderthal man. These were probably two races of people, or they may have been subspecies of a people that lived as contemporaries. There is some evidence that seems to show that the Cro-Magnons, the more modern of the two types, actually hunted down and killed off the Neanderthals, the more crude-looking and primitive species. Neanderthal remains have been found in Asia, in Northern Africa, and all over parts of Europe. Of all the kinds of fossil men known, the Neanderthal was the most widely distributed.

A careful check of the remains of late ice-age humans shows that even the earliest skulls found include among them variations that clearly indicate the presence of racial distinctions among human beings of the time. There are skulls from Africa and Southern Europe that appear to show Negroid characteristics; and there are many skulls from all parts of Europe, Southern Asia, and Africa which anticipate some of the modern racial traits that exist in these same places today. In every case, however, skeletal remains are not absolute indicators of physical appearance, and there must have been physical traits of major importance that do not show in the bone.

At this point, the relatively new science of cultural anthropology, with the help of archaeologists and ethnologists, begins the interpretation of man's progress from about the middle of the ice age to the present. The paleontologists' work has been superseded by the advent of culture. The cultural anthropologists help distinguish the races of mankind by fitting together the picture of the society in which he lived, what he hunted, what he ate, the tools he used, and so forth. This scientific data also makes it evident to researchers that the modern racial distribution of peoples was foreshadowed by the distribution and perfection of weapons and tools. These cultures are being excavated by archaeologists all over the world.

When the continental glaciers of the Pleistocene Epoch moved down over Northern Europe for the fourth and final time, the human beings who were living there were able to stay and survive the cold and other hardships that were imposed upon them by the advancing wall of ice. This climate and the solution to the problems of cold that it presented is regarded as a very important stimulant to the development of the rich culture of Europe that, later, set a pattern for the rest of the world.

One of the basic teachings in anthropology holds that the culture of any man or race is based on the biological factors that are operating prior to that culture's growth. One example of this is the fundamental desire of all animals to stay alive. During the ice age, man was faced with a biological fact that he could not alter. He could not stop the ice. Nor could his own body suddenly provide him with warmth in the form of fur or a new kind of fat layer to help him survive.

At this point culture went to work for ice-age man. We know that he had discovered the value of fire before that time, and his hands, his eyes, and his ability as a hunter provided the means to make clothing. So man of that time had two cultural elements— clothing and fire—that helped him survive a biological element that could easily have wiped him out.

Progress in Tools and Weapons

A. From the number and variety of animal bones found mixed with the bones of *Australopithecus,* it is assumed that this man-like ape knew how to utilize sticks and stones to help him kill the food he ate. Since monkeys utilize sticks and stones in an elementary way to help them hunt, this does not seem unlikely, especially since *Australopithecus* had apparently already evolved a good deal beyond the monkey level of specialization.

B. There is no direct evidence of the kind of tools or weapons that the Java man might have used, but there have been repeated efforts to prove a connection between the eoliths, or crude early Stone Age tools, that have been found in Europe with this type of man or perhaps one who lived at an even earlier time. It is only logical to assume that these people might have used clubs and very crude, unfashioned stones. Primitive peoples in the world today are able to do remarkable things with a sharpened stone that to the average person looks absolutely unworked. In some instances they are even able to cut down

35

trees simply by pounding at them with a sharp stone.

C. Peking man, whose remains have been discovered in caves of China, is considered slightly younger than Java man. There is definite evidence that the Peking people had fire; how they used it is very questionable. There is also abundant evidence that they smashed open bones to eat the marrow. To some, this implies that these men might also have known how to cook their food partially, at least. To others this means nothing more than that they had fire and kept warm.

D. Rhodesian man and other primitive types that occupy the time space between Peking man and the later Neanderthal types might have encountered fire and learned at least to keep warm with it, for in the lands they occupied there was frequent volcanic activity. It is possible that curious human beings could have found burning sticks and learned how to nurse them into full-fledged fires. Probably the chief hunting tool of the times was a sharp, hard stick used as a spear. Such a tool or weapon can kill a great many kinds of animals, especially slow-moving, soft-bodied animals that would have been a great part of primitive man's diet.

E. The Neanderthals, who lived successfully for so long a period, had learned to chip tools from flint and knew how to fasten spear points to shafts. But on many Neanderthal sites there is absolutely no evidence that fire was used either for warmth or for cooking. How this human being could have survived the climate of his time without a fire is a puzzle. The

Manlike ape of South Africa
(*Australopithecus*)

A

Erect ape-man of Java
(*Homo erectus*)

B

Erect ape-man of China
(*Homo erectus*)

C

Rhodesian man
(*Homo sapiens*)

D

Neanderthal man (*Homo sapiens sapiens*)

E

only possible answer is that we do not yet know enough about him. Only a relatively few sites have been excavated, and although some expeditions have specifically looked for evidences of fire at Neanderthal sites, none of them has been fortunate enough to find it yet.

It is significant that practically all of the primitive hunting people of the world keep fire whether or not they cook with it. They use it primarily to keep away dangerous beasts, and, of course, they use fire to keep warm. Apparently many of these present-day primitive peoples did not know how to make fire until Europeans taught them. Learning to use fire was one of the great distinguishing traits that set man apart from the other animals.

LIVING PRIMATES

PEN-TAILED TREE SHREW OF MALAY
AND BORNEO (PTILOCERCUS)

TYPICAL TREE SHREW (TUPAIA)

TREE SHREWS (*Tupaioids*)

THESE ARE small squirrellike animals that live in the forested southern countries of the Orient. Tree shrews were formally added to the list of primate mammals only recently. Before that, there was doubt whether they were anatomically true shrews of the insectivore order or primate mammals. The fact that doubt existed for so long leads to the conclusion that primates at some very early time in their evolutionary process might have broken away from a stock of animals that were insectivores.

The most common genus of tree shrew is the *Tupaia,* a Malay word, meaning squirrel or quick, that gives the whole group its name.

The five fingers and toes of this tree-dwelling animal are tipped with sharp claws, but otherwise the distinctive fingers and toes are primate in structure and use. It is this part of the animal's anatomy that is the chief reason tree shrews are placed in the primate group. When feeding, the food is held and moved freely by their hands; they sit up to eat, much as any squirrel does, and will eat almost anything. Observers who see tree shrews regularly in the wild state claim that their general behavior indicates a primate relationship. The bare-tailed, or pen-tailed, tree shrew shown in the illustration is smaller and more specialized than the *Tupaia.*

41

SLENDER LORIS (LORIS)

SLOW LORIS (NYCTICEBUS)

LORIS (*Lorisoids*)

LORISOIDS illustrate the next anatomical step upward in primate mammal development. The name loris is derived from a word meaning clown, and it was originally applied to the ridiculous-looking slow loris of Indonesia. Within the loris group as a whole there are many distinguishable species and subspecies.

Loris are slow-moving, deliberate animals, with very large eyes that appear to be watering all of the time. The fur is soft and thick, and the grasping ability of the fingers and toes is unique. Like other primates, these animals have nails on their fingers and toes, but they also have a peculiarly shaped claw that is used to extract insect food from crevices and similar tight places. They move around at night in search of food, which consists of vegetable matter and some insects. None of them has much tail; what there is is usually hidden in deep fur.

The slow loris, largest of the species, is sixteen inches long. The slender loris is half its size and has considerably thinner legs and much larger eyes. The slender loris eats less vegetable food, and its hands and feet show more specialization for hunting than those of other loris.

There is considerable variation of body markings in the loris family. Circles and stripes bordering the eyes help define some of the species.

ANGWANTIBO (ARCTOCEBUS)   POTTO (PERODICTICUS)

POTTOS

THE POTTOS and the angwantibos are a subfamily of the loris family that lives in Africa. Both animals are bulkier and fatter-looking than the Asiatic loris, and the eyes are very large, which is usual in animals of nocturnal habits. The sharp tips on the vertebrae of the neck are an interesting feature of the potto. These tips project through holes in the skin on the back of the neck and are used as weapons for butting with that area of its body.

The angwantibo is a smaller version of the potto. Its face is more sharp-looking; the ears are more prominent than in any other species in this family. The hands and feet of both these species show further modification for the primate abilities of grasping. They also have more special feeding habits. In the potto, the second fingers and second toes have been modified into short stumps for some unexplainable reason. Both animals eat fruit, insects, birds, and lizards. Ordinarily pottos are slow-moving, especially when stalking food. Perhaps that is why natives call the potto "Softly-Softlies." They catch unwary birds with a very fast pounce and grasping action of the hands.

In appearance and habits there is little outward evidence that these and related animals are primates. But the distinctive use of the hands and feet are primate traits; the internal structure of the animals is also definitive.

43

GALAGO, THE MOHOLI BUSH BABY (GALAGO SENEGALENSIS)

GALAGOES (*Galaginae*)

BUSH BABIES, or galagoes, represent another anatomical step upward among primate mammals. The typical galago lives in the dense forest areas of Africa, and all of them look and act quite differently from the preceding lower forms of primates. They retain the large eyes and sharply pointed faces of the lemurs, but their ears, their tails, and their feet have materially changed in form, and the animal uses these parts somewhat differently from the slower-moving loris and pottos.

Galago fur is very soft and thick, and the tail is used, like a squirrel's tail, as a balancing organ and as an aid to breaking a fall when traveling through the trees. These animals are not necessarily active nighttime animals, although they are more at home moving about under cover of darkness.

Galagoes eat a variety of food, including more vegetable matter than many of the other related primates eat. The tips of the fingers and toes have enlarged pads which would seem to be an aid to grasping. These enlarged grasping surfaces are typical of most of the lower forms of primates; it is usually the thumb of the hand and what would correspond to the big toe of this animal that exhibits the most grotesque enlargement.

The lower primates do not do well in zoos, and until recently they were little known outside their native lands. Air travel has now made more living study specimens available. The anatomy of all the lower forms of primates has been studied intensively in recent years in order to try to determine accurately a possible order of descent and relationship between these rather rare and variable animals.

44

AYE-AYE (DAUBENTONIA)   MOUSE LEMUR (MICROCEBUS)

LEMUROIDS—Unusual Types

THE LEMURIFORMES are a well-known infraorder of primates that were once considered the most basic primate type of mammal. The smallest lemur is hardly bigger than a mouse, and the largest is about the size of a medium-weight dog totaling four feet in length.

The aye-aye is the lowest and most doubtful form of lemur. These animals are structurally so different from other lemurs that they are only classed with them at all because of internal structures that can be seen only after dissection. The aye-aye's fur, a combination of coarse guard hairs and rather soft underfur, is rough, and the wide-spreading fingers and toes are peculiar. One finger of the hand is narrowed and lengthened into a special tool for extracting grubs and snails from points of concealment. The upper and lower front teeth are another peculiarity; they look like those of a rodent.

The smallest primate is the lesser mouse lemur, shown in the illustration behind the aye-aye. As its name suggests, it is mouse-sized and, like the aye-aye, it builds a round nest that looks quite like a mouse or rat's nest. Unlike most primates, these tiny animals go into a semidormant condition during the hot dry season of the year. Insects are their chief food.

COMMON LEMUR (LEMUR CATTA)

TYPICAL LEMURS

WOOLLY LEMURS and silky lemurs typify the Lemuriform group of animals best. These are the larger species and as their name suggests, their fur sets them apart at a glance. Lemurs sometimes band together as monkeys do; they feed at almost any time of the day, moving about on the ground in loose-knit groups.

These animals have foxlike faces, and their nostrils are in the tip of the snout. The arrangement and shape of the teeth also differentiates them from other primates. Most species of lemurs are found on the island of Madagascar, and there the species vary according to the climate and the density of the forested land they inhabit.

Lemurs range in color from mostly black to a light yellowish brown, and they may have banded tails and tufted ears. Their facial markings are often very beautiful. The face of the silky lemur is not furred. One species, the indri, has only a rudimentary tail. At ease, their movements are slow and deliberate, but when aroused or in danger they can move with great speed. Though they look like monkeys, lemurs habitually descend trees backward as the larger apes do. They eat a variety of food. Some appear to be especially fond of insects; others prefer fruit or are exclusively leaf eaters.

The many species of lemurs vary so much, one from the other, in their particular habits and in the great variety of markings in the fur that they have been studied in detail by anatomists. The common ring-tailed lemur, *Lemur catta,* is the species seen most often in zoos.

46

TARSIERS

(*Tarsiiformes*)

TARSIERS are small animals, about the size of a squirrel, with a long, slender hairless tail and a large head. Fifty to sixty million years ago they were widely distributed throughout the world, but today they are rather rare. The sole survivors of a once numerous animal group, they live in the Netherlands Indies and the Philippine Islands.

These little animals have many basic primate features, and a few scientists who specialize in the study of primate anatomy think that tarsiers might possibly have been the main branch from which all manlike creatures evolved. This is not a popular concept; it is based largely upon the relative abundance of extinct forms. Tarsierlike remains are variable and numerous enough to suggest that they may well bridge the gap between lemurs and all higher primates. The presence of fossil tarsiers and lemurs in ancient Eocene rocks has caused much speculation about the age of all other primate forms, which were once generally assumed to be recent animals.

Like many of the lower primates, tarsiers are active at night. Because of this, they have tremendous eyes to see their prey and any possible danger. For the most part, they eat insects, though lizards and similar small animals are sometimes part of their diet.

The name tarsier comes from the unusually large tarsus bone in the arch of the foot which, coupled with the next joint, provides an unusual apparatus that makes it possible

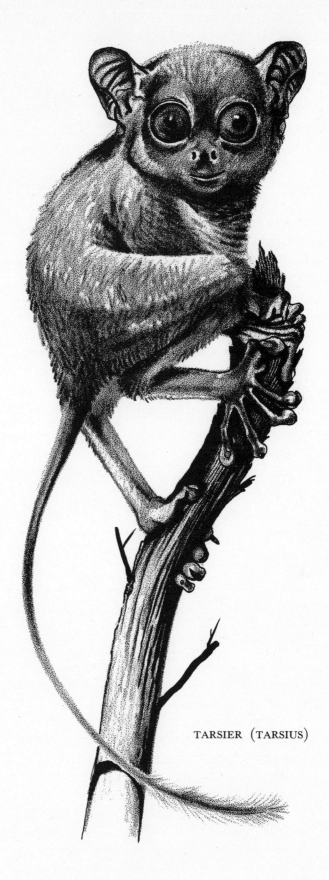

TARSIER (TARSIUS)

47

for the animal to leap long distances. When jumping, the tarsier seems to be projected, almost as if he were propelled by a spring.

The toes of the tarsier are long and slender, and all of the digits on the hands and feet have enlarged pads with a nonskid surface. These enable the animal to move about with sure-footedness under cover of darkness.

The numerous structural differences between the hands and the feet—in fact, between the entire front and back leg—of lemurs, tarsiers, and other animals is one of the major reasons they have been included in the primate order. Such functional and structural fore and hind leg differences are considered advanced animal features.

Another obvious anatomical peculiarity of the tarsier is its gigantic forward-looking eyes. It is certain that stereoscopic vision is of prime importance to an animal's ability to live in trees successfully. In the tarsier this feature is a prominent one, and the effect that eye enlargement has on the brain is reflected in the brain size and rearrangement of its masses. Tarsiers generally have only one young at each breeding; this is also considered an advanced primate feature. The animals' teeth, another definitive part of anatomy, resemble those found in the higher primates. Tarsiers have claws on the second and third toes; the other toes and fingers have narrow nails.

Though distinctly a primate, the tarsier is not anatomically close to the high degree of specialization found in monkeys, but it is far above the lemur level of development. The nose has become smaller, and the foxlike snout of the lemur is missing in the tarsier. Its face is sunken into the skull, the kind of face that is further modified in apes and man.

Some zoos display tarsiers, though the animal is delicate and has to be treated with great care. Its over-all body appearance is that of a gentle, soft-furred little animal, but this appearance is deceiving, for the tarsier can and does inflict a serious bite if disturbed. It is one of the grotesque animals of the world.

MONKEYS—
General

TYPICAL NEW-WORLD, FLAT-NOSED MONKEY

THE MONKEYS are a major division in the primate order of animals, but they do not figure in the evolution of man at all. They are a well-adapted group of animals that apparently ceased to evolve millions of years ago.

Monkeys have all of the advanced anatomical features that are present in the lemurs and tarsiers, developed to a greater degree and in many cases improved upon. A monkey's eyes are especially good and are regarded by anatomists as being functionally on a par with our own eyes. As in human beings, the ability to smell is no longer important to the monkey, and so the smelling apparatus is much reduced; the nose is also small.

The brain of a monkey is quite large in proportion to its body size, and one of the disquieting features about this entire group of animals is their near-human facial appearance. The shape of the skull, and the piercing look of the eyes furthers this resemblance, and the apparently insatiable curiosity of monkeys, which is amusing and often amazing, is considered very human. The eyes of the monkey help him satisfy his curiosity, and his free-moving arms and hands make it possible for him to do more with objects that interest him. He can pick them up and handle them— something other animals cannot do at all.

All monkeys are divided into two groups: the flat-nosed and the narrow-nosed monkeys. All of the species that live in Central and

TYPICAL OLD-WORLD, NARROW-NOSED MONKEY

49

GOLDEN LION MARMOSET (LEONTOCEBUS)

NEW-WORLD SPECIES

(*Ceboids and Hapaloids*)

PLATYRRHINE (FLAT-NOSED) MONKEYS

NO ONE KNOWS how many kinds of monkeys there are in the world, for many interbreed freely, and many others are scarcely known because they live in high treetops or in situations that prevent adequate observation. South America is particularly rich in animal species, including monkeys, that are poorly known to science.

Those who classify animals tend to set the marmosets aside in a special group of their own. These little animals are less active than

South America are flat-nosed monkeys. Their proper scientific name, Platyrrhini, simply means flat-nosed. The monkeys of Asia and Africa, including the apes, are called Catarrhini. These narrow-nosed monkeys have nostrils that point downward and are close together as in humans.

OWL MONKEY (AOTUS)   SQUIRREL MONKEY (SAIMIRI)

the monkeys; they are squirrellike in appearance. Nearly all of them have very thick, fine fur and long bushy tails. Their faces are short, and some slightly resemble a Pekingese dog's.

Some people consider marmosets primitive because they do not have the more specialized traits of monkeys, but it is possible that these so-called primitive traits actually could result from overspecialization and some measure of degeneration within the species. One example is found in the teeth—in man the last molar in the lower jaw is called a wisdom tooth; it sometimes grows out and sometimes does not. In

one very minor way, marmosets might be considered more specialized than human beings; through evolution they have lost a tooth that no longer functions for them.

By contrast, marmosets have retained one genuinely primitive feature; four of their toes have claws instead of flat nails. Their thumbs do not function as our thumbs do, and this is considered a degenerate condition.

All the other South and Central American monkeys also present interesting anatomical features and appearances to the observer. Chief among these is the way that many of

CAPUCHIN MONKEY (CEBUS)   WOOLLY MONKEY (LAGOTHRIX)

51

RED HOWLER MONKEY (ALOUATTA) SPIDER MONKEY (ATELES)

these monkeys are able to use their tails as a fifth hand. The spider monkey's tail is so well developed that the animal can actually pick up and pass objects to its hands or mouth with the tip. In many species, the tail is strong enough to support the monkey's weight without any help from the hands or feet.

The spider monkey is the most specialized of all the South American monkeys in every respect. This animal's adaptations to a tree-dwelling life are most complete. For example, the thumbs have almost completely disappeared; to aid his passage through the trees, they are reduced to simple stubs.

Paleontologists believe that all South American monkeys have been isolated on that continent since Eocene times. Because of this, they developed into many diverse forms with little molestation from predators, just as marsupial animals did in Australia. The ancestral development of the new-world monkey clan is still a major riddle. Scientists have not yet been able to explain why so many fossil forms of lemurs and tarsiers have been found in North America when, in South America, there was no diversity of monkey development beyond the present rather primitive flat-nosed animal. There is a wide variety of monkeys on that continent, however. Squirrel monkeys, owl monkeys, and howler monkeys are well-known common names, and there are many, many others.

It is obvious to anatomists that new-world monkeys are not as highly developed as are the monkeys of the old-world species and the great apes.

Major South American Monkeys

HAPALOIDS

Marmosets (Callithricidae)
Tamarins (Tamarin)
Goeldi's marmosets (Callimiconinae)
Titis (Callicebinae)

CEBOIDS

Half monkeys (Pithecinae)
Hand-tailed Monkeys (Cebinae)
Squirrel monkeys (Saimiri)

OLD-WORLD SPECIES
(*Simioids*)

CATARRHINE (NARROW-NOSED) MONKEYS

AMONG THE narrow-nosed monkeys, the average size seems to be greater than that observed among flat-nosed South American species. As their name indicates, the nostrils of catarrhine monkeys are close together and open forward and down. In many species tails are short or nonexistent.

Certain individual and family groups live part of their lives on the ground, and although many of them can readily climb trees, they do not as a matter of preference. On the ground, most apes, baboons, and monkeys move about on all fours rather than in an erect posture. Baby apes can move about freely while standing on their hind legs, but as they get older, their skeletal and muscular growth prevents them from walking erect without real effort.

Old-world monkeys anticipate human traits by being active in the daytime and sleeping at night. They have large brains, good stereoscopic vision, and front and hind legs which are quite different from each other in function and appearance. They have toenails rather than claws, and their breeding habits are very much like those of human beings.

Long before the first glaciers covered Europe, large numbers of monkeys and apes lived on that continent, and their remains have also been found in central Russia and in what is now the desert country of the Middle East. Living monkeys still thrive in many parts of the world that we do not think of as typical monkey habitats. There are monkeys in the Himalayas that dig in the snow for

PROBOSCIS MONKEY (NASALIS)　　　　　　GUEREZA MONKEY (COLOBUS)

food. They live as far north and as far up on the mountain sides as trees grow.

Within the monkey tribe there are some interesting deviations from what we commonly think of as monkey habits. One monkey species hunts other mammals in packs. Many types of monkeys swim easily, and some do so to hunt their food. The crab-eating monkey is an example. Actually, many species hunt sea food; they habitually live near beaches and in swamps where they can readily find the small water-dwelling animals that are a major part of their diet. In contrast, a surprising number of formidable-looking monkeys consume nothing but leaves as their basic food; others eat a varied diet of fruits and leaves, of insects, and other animal matter.

All narrow-nosed monkeys are divided into three large groups: the Colobine (Colobinae), the long-tailed monkeys (Cercopithecinae), and dog-faced monkeys (Cynopithecinae).

Colobine monkeys are generally large, with heavy bodies and long tails. They usually stay in tall trees of heavily forested areas. Among the familiar species are the guerezas, the langurs, and two anatomical extremes: the snub-nosed monkeys and the proboscis monkey. The male of this latter species sometime grows a nose three to four inches long.

The second group of monkeys, the long-tailed species, include the guenons, the mangabeys, the military monkeys, and the swamp monkey.

The dog-faced monkeys are the most highly developed group as a whole and include the macaques, best known and typified by the rhesus monkey, the "black apes" of the Celebes Islands, and the baboons of Africa.

BABOONS (*Papio*) AND OTHERS

Baboons are worth special consideration simply because they are among the most unusual looking of all mammals. These animals

54

HANUMAN MONKEY, A LANGUR
(SEMNOPITHECUS)

RHESUS MONKEY (MACACA)

DIANA MONKEY (CERCOPITHECUS)   RED-HEADED MANGABEY (CERCOCEBUS)
PATAS MONKEY (ERYTHROCEBUS)

ANUBIS BABOON (PAPIO ANUBIS)

GELADA
(THEROPITHECUS)

MANDRILL

DRILL
(MANDRILLUS LEUCOPHAEUS)

MANDRILL (MANDRILLUS SPHINX)

HAMADRYAS BABOON (PAPIO HAMADRYUS)

are fierce fighters; they live in large packs, roaming the rocky countryside while on the ground. Wherever they are numerous, they are destructive to cultivated crops, and in rare instances baboons have been known to carry off babies from native villages.

The most common baboon is the Anubis baboon, which ranges from coast to coast in Africa just north of the forested area. The most common species in the West African area is the Guinea baboon; in South Africa, it is the chacma, the largest of all baboons. The heavily maned Hamadryas baboon was once held sacred by Egyptians.

The chief natural enemy of baboons is the leopard, and if baboons are numerous in a region, the hunting of leopards is sometimes limited so the cats can help keep baboons in check. A large male baboon fighting a leopard single-handed can well hold its own. Its incisor teeth are long dangerous tusks, and its strength and courage are phenomenal.

Fighting a common enemy, a pack of baboons can easily rout any of the large predators and groups of hunting men as well. Fights between bands of baboons are fierce battles in which many individuals are slaughtered. Baboon troops are led by aggressive old males, who maneuver their charges the way a general maneuvers his troops on the field of battle. Activities within each group are highly organized, and under certain circumstances every animal from the youngest to the oldest individual has a specific job to do.

The gelada, a baboonlike primate found in Ethiopia, differs from other baboons in that it looks like a mandrill.

Drills and mandrills (genus *Mandrillus*) live in densely forested regions; both are large monkeys with colorful faces and fur. The males have muzzles of bright-colored naked flesh as well as highly colored calluses on the rump that are normal growths on all baboons. Calluses on the males are more colorful and larger than those of the females.

Monkey types that have a long face have a tendency for vegetable diets. They have thirty-two teeth, just as man has. This is a distinct correlation between man and the apes, and marks an evolutionary change from the original forty-four teeth that are found in more primitive basic mammalian stock.

Fossil monkeys found in the Old World date from Oligocene times; these were discovered first in Egyptian deposits thirty-five million years old. Like the fossil remains of ancient men, the important discoveries of fossil monkeys consist largely of jaws and teeth. Both the oldest-known monkey, called *Parapithecus*, and the oldest-known manlike ape, *Propliopithecus*, are known only from the remains of jaws and teeth. They are from the same geological deposit in Egypt, and their presence indicates a well-established anthropoid fauna at a period when other mammals had not achieved what we would consider a modern status.

GIBBONS (*Hylobates*)

THE HIGHEST primate division is that which includes the anthropoid apes, which range in size from gibbons to gorillas.

Gibbons are small animals compared to other anthropoids, but even so they are larger than most monkeys. Most of them weigh less than twenty pounds, and their slight build gives them a deceptively weak look. Their bodies are hairy, and their skin is black. The gibbon's forehead is low, but its normal acrobatic actions in the jungle and its apparently nonchalant passage through the treetops indicate that it has a highly developed sense of perception and quick motor reactions. In proportion to the body weight, the brain is quite large.

The gibbon's unusual ability to swing through the trees, though beautiful to observe, contributes toward making the animal difficult to classify, but the length of the arm, its joint structure, and fingers are distinctive from that of the monkeys and the other apes. The tusks of the male gibbon, which are long, and the calluses on the rump make them resemble baboons. These are points in which they differ from the other great apes.

Gibbons are extremely vocal animals and have calling contests between individuals and between entire troops. The color of their fur varies from almost solid black with just a faint bar of white over the eyes, to almost pure white hair on the entire body. The face is naked; the palms of the hands and feet are dark and hairless.

These animals spend some time on the ground. Occasionally they run on their hind legs, holding their hands and arms above their heads as balances and in order to clear the ground. Since the arm is about two and one half times the length of the body, it would otherwise drag on the ground when the animal walks. Sometimes gibbons also carry small objects this way. The gibbon's legs and torso are more nearly identical in proportion to those same body parts in man than are those of other apes.

These animals have no tails, and the big toe is separated from the remainder of the foot. The generally small size of gibbons is one of the chief reasons why they are placed lower on the scale of primate evolution than other apes.

Gibbons live in southeastern Asia. Some live in Sumatra; others are found in the central Himalayan area, Burma, and into Indo-China and Java. Gibbon species include the large siamang, the hoolock, the white-handed, the agile, and the silvery gibbon. All are clean, intelligent, and gentle in captivity. When they exercise in large cages in zoos, their graceful, swinging motions give the impression that their arms are elastic.

LAR GIBBONS   CONCOLOR, OR WHITE-CHEEKED GIBBONS

ORANGUTANS (*Pongo*)

THE ORANGUTAN has never been seriously considered a part of the direct evolution of living men; it is thought to be one of those isolated animals that has been passed up by evolution. It lives, doomed to extinction, in Borneo and Sumatra.

This animal is considerably bigger than any previously mentioned ape or monkey. It occasionally stands as high as five feet tall and weighs up to 200 pounds. In contrast to its very weak legs and feet, its arms and hands are enormous, but its arms are not as long in proportion to the body as are those of the gibbon. The knuckles of the hand very nearly reach the ground when the animal stands erect.

The orang has a weird appearance (its name means "forest man"), and in certain lights the reddish-orange hair looks mossy. The skin is generally dark, and the hair on the back of old males can grow to almost three feet in length. The face of an orang isn't as fierce-looking as that of a gorilla, for the great ridges of bone that give the gorilla its mean look are absent. The jaws and teeth do project well away from the rest of the face, however. Old animals have a mustached and bearded look that gives them a rather pleasant and friendly appearance, and they also have a peculiar fat pad around the cheek region that flattens the sides of the face and makes it bulge sideways. Old males nearly always have a tremendous pouch of skin below the throat which hangs down like a huge flat sack; it is thought to offer some protection to the throat when the males fight.

The orangs' poorly developed feet and legs are a clear indication that they can not and do not habitually move around on the ground. They prefer to stay in trees, although even there they cannot move swiftly through the smaller branches because of their great weight. They must move cautiously, and they spend considerable time testing the weight of branches on which they are about to travel.

When they bed down for the night these animals build very crude nests in low tree branches, and in some cases they cover their heads and upper body with big flat leaves as a protection against wetness. Orangs make all possible efforts to stay away from human beings. They live in the deepest forest they can find and only venture from it when pressed hard by man, yet when young animals are captured they show a surprising ability to learn, and they often behave in much the same way that very young human children do.

Their diet is widely varied, consisting mostly of vegetables, although in zoos orangs eat almost anything that is offered them. In captivity the adult animals spend much time in relaxed positions, usually on a large platform where they seem to take particular pleasure in "hiding," folding their long arms over their faces and heads while asleep. They are rather untidy in appearance, and bits of straw and other refuse from the cage may adhere to their coarse hair. Their thick, long fingers contrast strongly with their rather thin, delicate-looking arms and the pale skin on the underside of their bodies.

Among all of the higher apes, individual animals differ one from the other almost as markedly as human beings differ. Adult orangutans vary in appearance and temperament, too, but they tend to be gentler than other large monkeys or apes.

Size, general body plan, and to some extent the habits of the orangutan place it between the gibbon and the chimpanzee in the primate group, but none of its anatomical features are near-human enough to warrant including orangs in the line of primate progression that leads to man. This animal is a specialized development among primates that has been protected for centuries by geographic isolation.

ORANGUTANS (PONGO)

CHIMPANZEES (*Pan*)

CHIMPANZEES are apes that seem to possess so many nearly human traits that the average zoo visitor finds it impossible not to compare them to human beings. Its total appearance and its reactions to carefully planned test situations have provided much useful data about the learning limitations of higher primates.

A chimp is a forest animal that comes down to the ground readily to feed and to travel through the jungle. A full-grown male chimpanzee is powerful and quite large. He may stand over five feet in height, with body proportions very much like those of man. The adults do not generally weigh as much as orangs, although occasionally one may weigh as much as 200 pounds.

Chimpanzees build nests about thirty feet in the air, which are simple affairs made of bent-over twigs and interlaced branches placed at the base of large limbs. They travel and live in the forests in loosely knit family groups of from seven to fifteen individuals.

Like many animals dwelling in the dense African forest, the chimp is poorly known in its native habitat. Practically all knowledge of its habits has been derived from observations of captive animals. In captivity, the chimp has been given endless tests to determine its relative intelligence; it is clear that they can reason as well as remember. Chimpanzees have been able to use clubs and other simple objects as tools to achieve certain goals, and they can be trained to do many stunts. Some seem to enjoy dressing in clothing.

In most of its native habitat the chimp is not a rare animal. They are bolder than gorillas, and if they attack, the consequences are apt to be more serious. Unlike the gorilla, the chimp does not stop its charge; it follows through the threat.

The face of an adult chimp is not pretty, but the range of its facial expressions has always given it a special appeal to zoo visitors. The lips are thin and flexible, and the front teeth are formidable-looking, though the back teeth look nearly human. Faces are generally hairless and are often white.

These animals are noisy both in captivity and in their native haunts. They eat birds' eggs, rodents and other meat items, as well as the usual fruit and vegetable matter that all apes consume. Adventuresome researchers studying animal behavior have frequently attempted to rear young chimpanzees along with their own children to observe the progress of learning.

CHIMPANZEES (PAN)

GORILLAS (*Gorilla*)

GORILLAS are in many respects structurally similar to human beings, yet the gap that separates any of the great apes from man is very large. This is an acceptable statement to anthropologists, though some may differ in their opinion as to just how closely man and any of the great apes are related.

Gorillas and men rank well among the largest of all mammals. Male gorillas are known to reach a height of six feet or more and weigh from 300 pounds to as much as 600 in captivity. The hair and skin of a gorilla is usually black, but as the gorilla grows older its hair may turn gray or almost pure white.

The most striking feature about this animal is its tremendously massive neck and mean-looking face, dominated by a prominent brow over the eyes, a broad nose, and a bony crest that runs across the top of the skull. This great crest of bone is present only in the male. In spite of the fact that the gorilla has many human features, the least human of these are found in the face and jaws. The jaw is particularly large and is filled with formidable teeth. The nose is flat and lies nearly flat on the facial plane. Lips are thin and mobile; the ears are small.

Contrary to popular belief, gorillas seldom move about freely in trees. They prefer to walk on all fours, using the outside of their feet and their knuckles for support. A simple nest may be built in low branches, but more often it is on the ground. It consists of leaves and some branches laid flat.

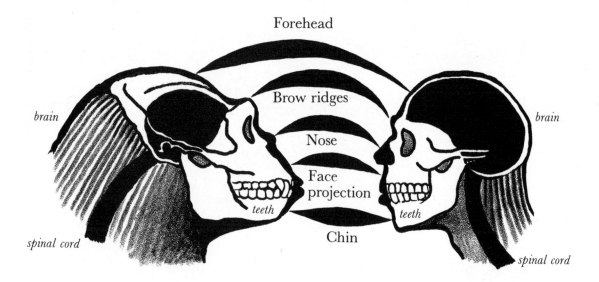

MAN AND THE GORILLA ARE THE "CLOSEST" PRIMATES STRUCTURALLY, BUT HOW DIFFERENT THEY ARE

GORILLAS (GORILLA)

Gorillas are primarily vegetarians, but they also consume a tremendous quantity of grubs and insects. The most famous captive gorilla of all time was Bushman. When he died an autopsy revealed a startling vitamin deficiency, in spite of the best care by zoo dieticians. The zoo had neglected to give the huge gorilla such simple but significant things as insects to help keep him healthy.

The hand of a gorilla is short and wider than that of other apes. The thumb is well developed, but shorter than that of a man, and the fingers are partially webbed. If the animal has normally developed feet, they rest flatter on the ground than do the feet of other apes; in this respect they are nearly human. Though these great apes are among the strongest of animals, they are seldom aggressive in carrying out threats to human beings. They bluff in many ways—making fierce short rushes, screaming, and beating their chests with open hands. There have been a few cases when a gorilla, apparently not realizing its strength, literally ripped a person apart with one sweep of its powerful hand. In spite of such occurrences the natives in Africa do not fear a gorilla as much as is commonly believed. Most naturalists who have studied the animal in the wild repeat the observation that the gorilla is not as aggressive as he is generally thought to be. Individual gorillas vary temperamentally as much as men do.

In reviewing the body characteristics that separate man from the great apes, scientists have agreed that the chimpanzee and the gorilla are closer to man in structure than they are to lower apes. These two species have fewer anatomical features in common with the lower apes then they have with human beings.

From the scientific point of view, man is properly classed as a primate. He is structurally related to primates and logically would have descended from a primate in the distant past. In Darwin's time, people looked at external body features in making their comparisons. Today, geneticists and blood specialists have given us additional information to add to the gross anatomical features that show these two great apes and man to be quite close structurally. It should be made clear, however, that no one in the anthropological field feels that man is a direct descendant of either the chimpanzee or the gorilla. These animals are simply the living creatures whose total appearance helps verify the story of animal evolution and happens to be the closest point to man's station in the scheme of life.

THE EVOLUTION OF MAN

The Distant Ancestry of Monkeys
and Apes

THE OLDEST-KNOWN fossil monkey is *Parapithecus frassi,* and evidence of its existence came from Oligocene rocks thirty-five million years old. To date, the only available record is a single lower jaw in which the teeth are so definitive that anatomists have been able to deduce that this animal must have been one of the very early ancestors of all the living narrow-nosed (catarrhine) monkeys that inhabit the Old World.

The size of this monkey's teeth plus the arrangement of the cutting surfaces on the molars and premolars have led specialists to consider it as the most ancestral monkey form known. The sharp angle at which the two halves of the lower jaw fit together is also regarded as primitive. From such meager evidence it is supposed that this animal might have resembled almost any of the generalized African monkeys of today, but it was small—the jaw being only one and one half inches in length.

Rocks from Pliocene times, deposited twenty to twenty-five million years later, have yielded remains of fossil monkeys from a wide geographic area of the Old World. One of the best-known extinct monkeys is *Mesopithecus.* From this animal's nearly complete and fairly numerous remains it is evident that monkeys were thriving in many places throughout Europe, and that they had begun to diversify into some of the many types that are alive today in only the tropical parts of the world.

Animals that could be the ancestors of the anthropoid apes or man are distinctly different from the earliest monkeys. For the beginnings of this animal group one has to refer again to the Lower Oligocene soils of Egypt where another single jaw is the fossil evidence upon which the origin of an entire group of animals is based.

This jaw is slightly larger than that of the oldest monkey, but it is still much smaller than that of any living ape. The grinding surface of teeth in the jaw shows a pattern that is in contrast to that of living monkeys and very much like that of the great apes. The bony portion of the jaw is also deeper and more robust, much like those of the present-day higher apes. The name of this earliest ape is *Propliopithecus haeckeli.*

Searching the fossil record for later, more advanced forms of apes and apelike men we must refer to bones from the Lower Miocene

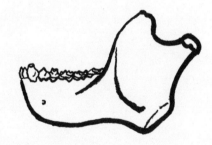

Parapithecus (monkey)

Propliopithecus (manlike ape)

SINGLE JAWS
each is the oldest of its kind known

69

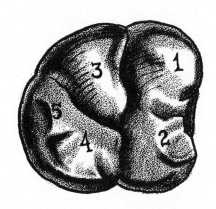

THE Y5 PATTERN IN THE MOLAR OF
DRYOPITHECUS FRICKII

Epoch, approximately twenty million years ago. These represent another phase of the evolutionary history of the primates. The first of these fossils was found in Africa; since that time many similar varieties have been found in Europe and in Asia as well. Most of the specimens consist of loose teeth; they fall into a pattern that has been well-defined and is easily recognized because it is so distinctive.

From the size of the teeth it seems that some individual animals might have been

PROCONSUL AFRICANUS
(A mixture of ape and human structural traits)

70

larger than the living gorilla, but they were a variable group. They are best typified by one which has been called *Dryopithecus* (meaning oak ape) *frickii.*

The molars of *Dryopithecus* and its relatives are of special interest because their grinding surface consists of a series of cusps split by a Y-shaped groove. This pattern is significant because it is next seen in the teeth of the earliest true men. Thus it would seem that these apelike creatures could have been close to the ancestral line of man and the great apes as well. Many of these variable ape species have been found in close association with the remains of lemurs and monkeys. The strongest line of development that can be discerned in their remains is a skeletal pattern that resembles the framework of the gibbon.

In Asia a form similar to *Dryopithecus* has been found; it is called *Sivapithecus.* The canine teeth of this specimen are modified and shortened, very much like those of man, and in the jawbone itself there is a slight hint of a chin, a distinctively human feature. These two animals seem to represent a combination of anatomical structures that typify one important plateau in the development of the apes and near-human forms. For this reason, the name *Dryopithecus-Sivapithecus* has been given this over-all group of fossil animals to indicate their stage of physical specialty. Parts of skeletons representing both these animals and their relatives have been found in various deposits that span a long period of time, approximately twenty million years. The length of the time they span is an indication of their success and strengthens the view that they are vital to all primate progress.

The best and most complete remains of a fossil ape that have been found up to this point in the earth's history belong to an animal called *Proconsul africanus.* This ape was big, and several individual specimens are known. These include bones of some young animals as well as those of at least one fully adult male animal.

The form of the lower jaw, the structure of the teeth, and the arrangement of the teeth in this animal are important, but in *Proconsul* the

GEOLOGIC NAMES	Monkeys	Apes	Australoids	Negroids	Mongoloids	Caucasoids	Bushmen	IMPORTANT HUMAN TYPES	YEARS
Holocene Epoch									
									10,000
									50,000
Fourth Glacial Period					Cro-Magnon			Practically all of the well-known discoveries of ancient men date after this point	100,000
			Rhodesian	Skhūl	Boskop Man			Late Java Man	
			Neanderthal Tabun						200,000
Third Glacial Period									
									300,000
									400,000
								Paranthropus Peking Man	
									500,000
Second Glacial Period								Heidelberg Man Kanam	
								Earliest Java Man Australopithecus (manlike apes)	
First Glacial Period Pleistocene Epoch Quaternary Period								Nearly all of our well-known mammals were thriving by this time	1 million
									5 million
Pliocene Epoch									10 million
								Pliopithecus Dryopithecus (oak ape)	15 million
									20 million
Miocene Epoch	NEW-WORLD MONKEYS	OLD-WORLD MONKEYS	APE STOCK		HUMAN STOCK			Often called the Golden Age of Mammals	25 million
									30 million
Oligocene Epoch								Split of primate stocks (approximately here) Proconsul (near-human type)	35 million
Tertiary Period began 70 million years ago								Propliopithecus	

CHART OF TERTIARY AND QUATERNARY PERIODS OF GEOLOGIC TIME

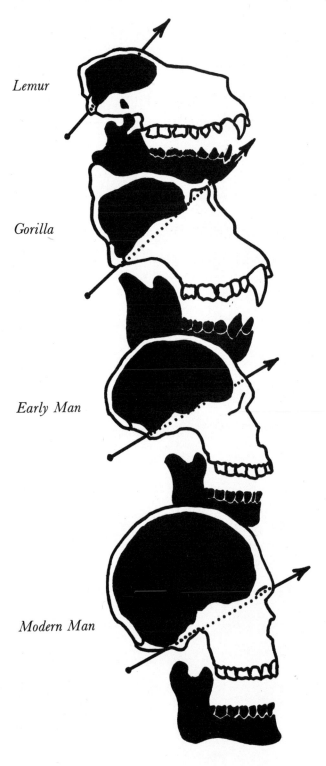

Lemur

Gorilla

Early Man

Modern Man

(not drawn to the same scale)

BRAINS BECOME LARGER
FACE AND JAWS ARE REDUCED

scientists have something else to work with—they have some of the bones of the heel and foot. From the form of these bones, it can be deduced that this animal had the muscle arrangements that would have enabled him to walk erect. It is possible that he did not, but at least his leg structure was such that he could have done so. This is the oldest fossil we have in which evidence of this peculiarly human trait can be read directly from the bones. *Proconsul* also had some anatomical structures that were not at all human, however. These are most evident in the teeth; the long sharp canines are particularly like those of modern apes or baboons.

Proconsul comes from East Africa, and the sites that have produced bones continue to yield important new finds. Many of these have not been described in book form, but it is anticipated that newer specimens will clear up one controversial point. Some scientists have said that *Proconsul* was an ancestor to the chimpanzee; others have contended that the chimpanzee had begun his evolution prior to the *Proconsul* form. At present the available evidence would seem to place *Proconsul* more nearly in line with man's development than in line with the development of the anthropoid apes.

Australopithecus and Related Animals

from South Africa

FROM 1924 until the present time, important geological deposits in South Africa have yielded numerous and varied animal fossils. On one hand, they have tended to clarify and, on the other hand, to further split scientists' notions about man's origins and his diversity. It is agreed that most of these animal remains represent a near-human form although one that is definitely still apelike in some traits. It is also generally agreed that these animals, called Australopithecines, occurred too late in geologic time to be considered the ancestors of man. They are, rather, a further division of the anthropoid group into a separate near-human line of evolution.

At least three major variations of this animal are known. The first and earliest to be discovered was called *Australopithecus,* the second was called *Plesianthropus,* and the third *Paranthropus.* Each of these variants was found in a different geological level, and each seems to represent a slightly different form of animal. Together they spanned a period of earth history totaling something like half a million years.

These South African animals were thriving when what we know as Peking man and Java man, considered true early human forms, were alive. Their many human traits are sufficient to set them aside from the great apes, but in view of their brain size alone, these animals cannot be admitted to the classification occupied by true men. The brains of Australopithecines were large but were well within the range of size found in the cranial capacity of the great apes. Their brain volume comes close to that of the most primitive men, but apes do not have what we would consider an adequate brain size for a normal human being today.

The assumed facial appearance of *Australopithecus* and its relatives seems to be about halfway between the projecting face of the largest great apes and the face of a human being. The jaws do not project as much as those of an ape; the nose and the placement of the eyes are modified to a near-human profile.

There are only fragmentary parts of the legs of these animals available, so some anatomists withhold judgment about their ability to walk erect. Nevertheless, the angle at which the upper leg bones fit into the sockets of the pelvis gives us reason to believe that it was possible for them to walk erect. The point at which the skull sets on the top vertebrae also indicates nearly erect posture. There is a definite agreement of opinion that these animals did live on the ground.

Dr. Robert Broom, who has had much to do with the discovery and description of *Australopithecus* and related forms, has described this animal as an active predator, probably dwelling in a cave. He deduces this from the remnants of other animals present in the same rock formation that produced the bones of *Australopithecus.* He also states that *Australopithecus* frequented plains areas, that he hunted in streams and in trees, that he cracked open bones to eat the marrow, and that he used some primitive weapons—probably sticks and unworked stones—to kill his game. He was very agile and retained many of the monkey's quick movements which

AUSTRALOPITHECUS (MANLIKE APE) OF SOUTH AFRICA

made it possible for him to catch lizards, rabbits, and other fast-moving game. Dr. Broom concludes that this animal had to exploit every possible source of food in order to exist in the harsh and pressing environment indicated by the evidence of habitat from which his remains have been taken. Dr. Broom also feels that though this animal was a vigorous hunter, it must have had some social instinct to group together, just as baboons of present-day Africa live and act as a pack.

All three Australopithecine types present unanimous evidence that the teeth of these animals were more human than apelike. This statement applies not only to the shape and size of the teeth but also to their sequence in the jawbones.

The most unsatisfactory portion of the story of these animals from South Africa is the uncertainty of dates for the deposits in which the bones occur. Dr. Broom thought that some of these deposits date from Pliocene times and that still others, laid down later, were from Pleistocene deposits. Today it is popular to think that all of the Australopithecines have come from early Pleistocene deposits and that some of the animals lived into Middle Pleistocene times.

The initial discovery of *Australopithecus africanus* in Taungs, a town in Cape of Good Hope province, in 1924 has been described by Dr. Raymond A. Dart. The specimen was the skull of a child not more than six years old, and though it represented a young individual, it was sufficiently complete to enable Dart's descriptive work to declare that it was an animal more human than apelike. Later discoveries have shown that the young of such animals more nearly resembled human beings than they did apes; adult forms apparently grew more and more apelike as they grew older.

Unfortunately for students of anthropology, the rich deposits of South Africa are still inadequately known outside of that continent. Many specimens have been tentatively described, but they have not been fully described in print. We can only hope that more research will continue in this rich and promising field.

Extinct Human Beings

THE PRIMITIVE MEN of the world are often categorized conveniently into three main groups: the ancient men, called the Archanthropinae; the old men, or the Paleoanthropinae; and the new men, called the Neoanthropinae. All of these human types were thriving before men began to use metals as an important part of their cultural progress.

Of the hundreds of specimens that make up this group of extinct men, only two discoveries were in existence when the great Charles Darwin published his book *The Origin of Species* in 1859. Even in 1871, when Mr. Darwin published *The Descent of Man,* his ideas about race and the descent of man were based on observing animals that were not human. His distinctive conclusions were based on good scientific observation and deductive work rather than actual human fossil specimens.

Since that time, an almost impossible series of names and relationships between the known specimens of extinct man have been proposed, but basically everyone agrees that human beings are a single genus, called *Homo,* and that living human beings are a single species, called *sapiens.*

In this book the most ancient men are typified by *Gigantopithecus* and *Meganthropus.* These fossil forms are discussed in this book under the title "Giants as Possible Ancestors." There was a third kind of ancient man, *Pithecanthropus erectus,* or as some modern anthropologists call him, *Homo erectus.* By now the story of Dr. Eugène Dubois' discovery of the erect ape-man from Java is quite well known.

Dr. Dubois found his specimen in the banks of the Solo River near Trinil in central Java. Had the relatively few teeth, the leg bone, and the skull cap he found remained the only discoveries of their kind, this type of human being would have always been considered a doubtful stage, but fortunately, after diligent searching, other specimens turned up in that same region. These finds bore out Dr. Dubois' conviction that the most primitive human types might be found in that general area of the eastern world. Unfortunately for anthropology there was so much discussion and ridicule of these specimens when their descrip-

PEKING MAN

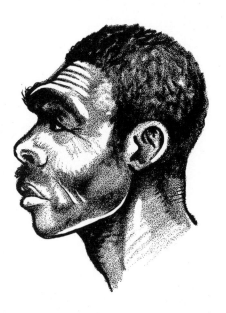

RHODESIAN MAN

PEKING AND JAVA MAN OF ASIA (HOMO ERECTUS)

tions were published, that Dr. Dubois withdrew them from public view for many years. When he did relent and bring them out from their place of safekeeping, he chose to reverse some of his earlier opinions and contend that the ape-man of Java was not an erect human type.

In over-all appearance the erect ape-man was of moderate height, about five and one-half feet tall. He had a sloping forehead, and his face and skull must have looked very much like an ape's. It was carried on the skeletal framework of a human body. The size of the brain of this human is almost twice that of a gorilla's.

Other skulls found near that original discovery spot include a species called *Homo modjokertensis* and one called *Pithecanthropus robustus*.

The now famous *Sinanthropus pekinensis* added to the story of the erect human beings. This Peking man is represented by fairly numerous remains, and though he was first described as a separate kind of erect ape-man, it was later concluded that his remains were so close structurally to Dubois' Java man that they should be lumped together as erect human beings of the same type.

The Java-man sites did not reveal any items that might have been used as tools or any other evidence of culture, but the Peking-man site did reveal that these people knew the use of fire. Apparently they also used very crude tools—stones that resemble eoliths, and clubs of wood.

Anthropologists are less positive about the possible relationship of Wadjak man (also found by Dr. Dubois) and *Homo soloensis* to other ancient men. The Solo man in particular seems to have some of the structural traits that are associated with Neanderthal man. Because of the kind of wooded country in which these crude half-brained human beings lived, there is little or nothing that can be discovered about their living habits or any possible cultural traits. Tropical vegetation and climate hasten the destruction of such evidence. Scientists know more about Peking man primarily because most of his remains were found in caves where they were relatively undisturbed. All other discoveries that date from this time, approximately 500,000 to 700,000 years ago, indicate that human beings were free-roaming, near-animal types that lived off the land very much as a band of gorillas might live off a forested tract. Even though the ancient men are very old, their total outward appearance was already quite human.

The next large group of human types are the Paleoanthropinae, the old men. A description of this portion of man's evolution must include the jaw of Heidelberg man, and it should also include a mention of Rhodesian man. The skull of this latter type indicates that the facial area must have been quite like a gorilla's. There is a tremendous apelike brow, but the teeth and the brain cavity within the skull place Rhodesian man in this intermediate evolutionary stage. This skull is one of the most astonishing among all those that tell the human story.

The distinctive skeletons that best represent this intermediate human type are those of the Neanderthal race. These were probably rough-looking people who lived in shallow caves and roamed over a great part of the world. They thrived for well over 100,000 years in spite of terrific hardships of climate and apparently great persecution at the hands of later Cro-Magnon-type people.

The Neanderthal is perhaps the best known of all the famous prehistoric men. Most people have seen reconstructions of the male head of the Neanderthal; he is shown as having a rather large nose, a projecting area beneath the nose, a receding chin, a thick neck, and a low brow. Though these men are called erect humans, neither the Neanderthal nor the preceding Peking or Java men actually walked fully erect. The head jutted forward, and most of them must have had a humpbacked appearance. The brain size of this human was very nearly modern.

The new men (Neoanthropinae) are best typified by the Cro-Magnon racial types and others whose cultures and anatomy had begun to look quite modern.

Eoliths

IN EUROPE unusually shaped stones have been found in soils that scientists think ought to contain human remains, although such remains are so far undiscovered. Anthropologists and archaeologists have argued for years over these interesting stones which they call eoliths, meaning "dawn stones." Some students think these shaped stones were man's earliest effort to make tools. To others these eoliths are simply pebbles and flakes, nicked and chipped by the violence of water tumbling rock and soil together.

At present no one can explain eoliths, but it is clear that if men have evolved as most people believe they did, simple tools ought to exist in the Pliocene soils that have produced eoliths. So long as more positive evidence of man's history is absent from these soils, there is a gap in the human story.

The living habits of the people who might have made such crude tools would have been so simple that skeletal evidence of their having lived at all was probably erased by nature very quickly after death.

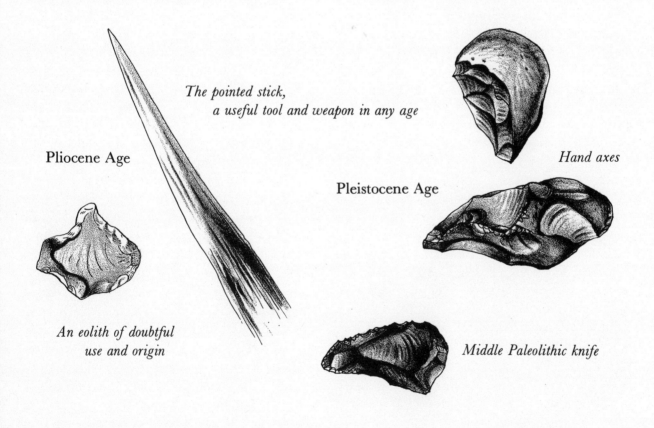

*The pointed stick,
a useful tool and weapon in any age*

Pliocene Age

Hand axes

Pleistocene Age

*An eolith of doubtful
use and origin*

Middle Paleolithic knife

PALEOLITHIC TOOLS

Giants as Possible Ancestors

DURING A PART of the great ice age a wide variety of mammals—camels, sloths, bears, elephants, and many others—became giants. Since large body size enables living northern mammals to better withstand the cold they encounter, it is believed that the larger bodies of ice-age mammals were one of the reasons that they, too, were able to thrive in the bitter cold of that time. One of the puzzling and yet very intriguing portions of man's prehistory also involves giants.

At least one anthropologist, Dr. Franz Weidenreich, has proposed the idea that present-day human beings evolved from a race of giants who lived on earth while the four-footed giants were still thriving. Teeth and a few skull bones are the basis for the theory, but all of the finds together represent no more than a half dozen individuals. When these fragments were first brought to light, most of them were thought to be abnormalities or, in one case, a difference in size between the male and female of the same species. Considered in order of discovery these specimens are:

Heidelberg jaw
FROM MAUER, GERMANY, FOUND IN 1907 BY DR. OTTO SCHOETENSACK

Of the specimens considered, this apelike jaw is perhaps least likely to have belonged to a giant, but a comparison to later discoveries has suggested the possibility. The great size of the jaw is not in keeping with the nearly normal size of the teeth, which are structurally human in all respects. Anatomists tend to regard such jaws as abnormalities rather than evidence of true giantism. Anthropologists suggest that this kind of man might have given rise to later Neanderthal types, since the heads of Neanderthal men were large in proportion to their body size.

Pithecanthropus robustus
FROM SANGIRAN, JAVA, FOUND IN 1938 BY DR. G. H. R. VON KOENIGSWALD

The Javanese localities that produced the first good records of primitive man later yielded additional skull bones and a partial jaw that have been designated *Pithecanthropus robustus*. The bones were initially thought to belong to a large male, *Pithecanthropus erectus*, but later reconstructions of the specimen led to its classification as a distinct subspecies. The broken bones belong to the thickest human skull that has ever been found. They would seem to support the giant-race theory because of the skull's strategic relationship to

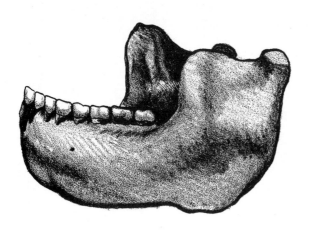

THE MASSIVE JAW OF HEIDELBERG MAN

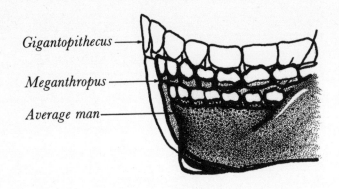

Gigantopithecus
Meganthropus
Average man

THE JAWS AND TEETH OF GIANTS

other Java-man sites, and because details of structure suggest a more primitive type of man. When the smashed bones were fully restored, the over-all appearance of the skull was apelike, though many obviously human features were present.

Meganthropus paleojavanicus
FROM SANGIRAN, JAVA, FOUND IN 1938 AND IN 1940 BY DR. G. H. R. VON KOENIGSWALD

Two jaw fragments of unusual proportions add to the story of human giants. These belonged to a chinless early man who ranged in size from an unusually big modern man to one ten or twelve feet tall.

The first jaw discovery had broken, worn teeth that did not permit accurate study. The second jaw piece had fine teeth that enabled detailed comparisons to those of the biggest apes and other early men. There was no doubt that the jaw is human, but the size of the man who carried it has long been vigorously disputed. To some, it is the jaw of a giant; to others this jaw falls just within the uppermost range of variation found among living men.

Homo modjokertensis
FROM MODJOKERTO, JAVA, FOUND IN 1936 BY DR. G. H. R. VON KOENIGSWALD

The discovery is of no value as a comparison to other specimens because the skull is that of a child less than one year old. The remains are important because they came from the Djetis level, a layer of earth beneath and therefore older than the soil that yielded the Java man and the bones of the Java giants. Such bones highlight the importance of Java and that entire Asiatic area in the distribution of earliest man and show that further evidence of value may be found there in the future.

Gigantopithecus blacki
FOUND IN PEKING AND HONG KONG IN 1903 BY SCHLOSSER, AND FROM 1935 TO 1939 BY VON KOENIGSWALD

The most unusual record of human giants is derived from loose teeth purchased in the drugstores of China. The first of these was a badly worn molar bought in 1903. It preceded the discovery of Peking man and was a clue to the possible presence of early human beings in that geographic area. Later, in Hong Kong, additional teeth were found, also in drugstores. These were in better condition, and their proportions slightly larger than those of the first big tooth.

The idea of hunting for teeth in a drugstore sounds strange unless one knows that many Chinese regard fossil bones and teeth as medicine; ground-up teeth are taken as a cure for toothache. Paleontologists have long hunted

HEIDELBERG MAN

81

for interesting fossils in Chinese drugstores. The main handicap to admitting such specimens as evidence is the virtual impossibility of placing them in an accurate geological horizon. By minute analysis of dirt still adhering to the specimens, by comparison to other animal remains brought in at the same time, and by knowledge of a collector's collecting grounds it is possible to determine an approximate location and date for "drugstore discoveries."

A tentative reconstruction of a jaw containing these giant teeth has been made, and although reconstructions of total body size based upon such flimsy support are hazardous, such a jaw would indicate a human being weighing at least 500 pounds and standing between ten and twelve feet tall.

The German paleontologist G. H. R. von Koenigswald, thinking them to be more apelike than human, declared his giant teeth to be those of an animal he called *Gigantopithecus*.

Later study has tended to include them with other intermediate primitive human forms. Since giantism is regarded as a primitive trait among mammals, it would be expected that such huge teeth would belong to a very crude and early form of human.

One of the main reasons why man's possible origin in a giant stock is even partially accepted is due to the deep respect anthropologists have for the detailed workmanship of Dr. Franz Weidenreich. His exhaustive studies cover every possible feature that has any bearing on the story of the ice-age giants, but the extreme scarcity of bones as evidence to support his theory has led many persons to ignore it entirely.

The question still remains whether giants were part of the main line of human evolution or whether they were a parallel development to the erect man of Java and China. In either case, the presence of huge men on the ice-age landscape is accepted as fact.

The Ice and Man

STUDYING human beings who lived during the many years that passed between the beginning of the ice age and the melting of the fourth big mass of glacial ice covering the Northern Hemisphere is difficult because there are barely more than 100 specimens available. These range from a few scraps of bone to nearly entire skeletons. About half of the total bones are those of Neanderthal types. All the others are teasingly interesting scraps that lead our thoughts along interesting paths which end abruptly when the scant material runs out. There is no other way of verifying our concept of what may have happened.

To many anthropologists, the fact that human beings lived in Europe during the final glaciation of that continent is tremendously significant. The growth of man's culture and ingenuity in meeting the problems of the ice age seems to mark a great turning point that eventually led to the tremendous cultural expansion that spread all over Europe, the Near East, and North Africa in the ages that followed.

One aspect of the ice age that some people overlook is the fact that when so much of the world was locked in ice, the trapped water in ice made many coastal parts of our continents dry land. There are many examples of this, but one of the most significant is the drying up of much of the Mediterranean Sea, with the result that Africa, Asia, and Europe were linked by dry-land bridges. It is possible that these were solid long enough for villages and farmlands to exist there for centuries.

Obviously the over-all weather in Europe was much different during the Pleistocene Epoch than it is today. One of the important effects of this difference is that places now inhospitable to man (for example, the Sahara Desert) were during those times green and perfectly capable of supporting well-developed civilizations.

In any assembly of animals in which the range of a species is broad, it is usually the most definitive types that live in the center of the range, and it is the variation of those types that live on the edge of the range. This is also true of human beings. The most advanced men of the ice age were clustered around the Mediterranean, either in Africa or Southern Europe. The less advanced Neanderthals apparently preferred to live near the edge of the ice-free lands where it was colder and more wet. The primitive South African people, in turn, lived at the other extreme of the human range where it was dry and nearly desert country. The culture of nearly all of these people was so poorly developed that there is difficulty in reconstructing exactly how they lived.

Tools and in some case their weapons are often the only means by which archaeologists have come to know these prehistoric men. Many of these tools were made of flint, for man discovered the unusual properties of flint very early. The study of these tools is difficult and frustrating but at present they are the only practical means we have of knowing the distribution and something of the habits of early ice-age human beings.

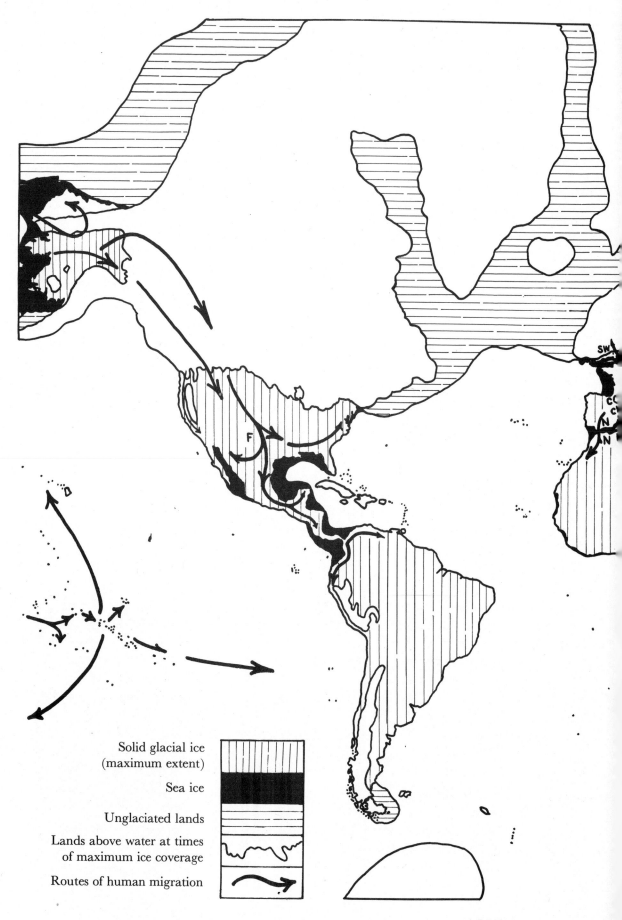

Solid glacial ice
(maximum extent)

Sea ice

Unglaciated lands

Lands above water at times
of maximum ice coverage

Routes of human migration

ANCIENT MAN

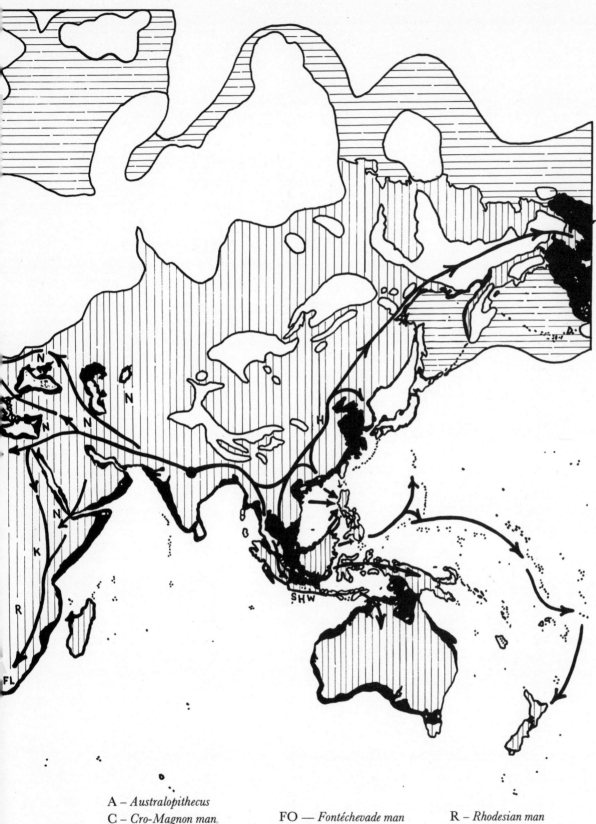

A – *Australopithecus*
C – *Cro-Magnon man*
CH – *Chancelade man*
F – *Folsom man*
FL – *Florisbad man*

FO — *Fontéchevade man*
H – *Homo erectus*
K – *Kanjera man*
N – *Neanderthal man*

R – *Rhodesian man*
S – *Solo man*
W – *Wadjak man*
SW – *Swanscombe man*

ATION TO THE ICE AGE

Neanderthal Man (Homo neanderthalensis)

EXCEPT FOR his inability to stand completely erect, the Neanderthal man was essentially modern. Judging from a footprint of this man that was found in a cave, the flat-footedness and low arch of the foot indicates that he was a slow-moving, rather plodding man. It is supposed that the Neanderthals knew how to use fire and that they made clothing of skins, for they certainly needed these skills to help them survive the severe cold of the ice age. They lived very close to the areas in Europe that were heavily glaciated, and the climate of the time was bitter. They made tools and weapons in a crude but efficient manner. They knew how to fasten spear points to shafts and apparently made various kinds of hammers and axes.

There are many variations from the basic Neanderthal type; several of these need mention. One is the skull that comes from Steinheim, Germany; the other is a specimen that comes from Ehringsdorf, Germany. In both of these remains the features of the skull suggest a blending of features between these old men and the men of the newer Stone Age.

Neanderthal skulls found at Mount Carmel in Palestine in 1932 have given support to the theory that modern men evolved from this stage of Neanderthaloid evolution. Another possibility is that recent man evolved some other place in the world and then migrated to Palestine where he interbred with this species. These Palestine finds also are supposed to prove beyond any doubt that the Cro-Magnon-type humans did not drive the Neanderthals into extinction. They may well have pushed them out of their home grounds in Europe toward North Africa or the Far East, but it is thought that the dating of the Mount Carmel skulls proves that at least they did not kill them off.

The Neanderthal is a popular kind of extinct human being because his big head and over-all crude appearance fit the average person's notion of what a Stone Age cave man ought to look like. The restorations of these men in the Museum of Natural History at Chicago and other places throughout the museum world have helped to strengthen this belief.

NEANDERTHAL MAN, A WIDESPREAD TYPE

A Craftsman Develops: *Homo sapiens sapiens*

THE NEW HOMINIDS are the final group of prehistoric human beings. They are typified by their fully modern brain size; in fact, the actual brain size of some Cro-Magnon people was apparently even greater on an average than that of many modern human beings. The Swanscombe man of England is considered the oldest of these new men. It is known only from the upper and back portions of a single skull.

Besides the classic Cro-Magnon type of man there are at least four others that scientists feel are worth separate mention. First are

SWANSCOMBE MAN
ONE OF THE EARLIEST FULL-BRAINED MEN

the Grimaldi skeletons, which are important because the type seems to have been a cross between white and Negroid. The Predmost from Czechoslovakia is a mixture with Neanderthals. The Combe-Capelle and the Fontéchevade man from France lived in the late ice age and represent a mixture of Neanderthal, Swanscombe, and basic Cro-Magnon types.

Most descriptions of prehistoric men end with the Cro-Magnon type; the over-all body height of these individuals and all the details of the skeleton correspond exactly with those of modern men. In addition, the Cro-Magnons were skilled artists whose cave paintings are known the world over for their beauty, accuracy, and implications of an extensive religious culture. The tools of this advanced human group show a high degree of skill in their manufacture; it is well known that they had rather elaborate social organizations, and that the people of certain groups hunted well together.

Literally millions of tools and weapons that link the story of the Cro-Magnon people with that of their environment and the animals they killed for food have been discovered. During this very long stage in the development of human societies, the most significant aspect of culture was the discovery of the properties in flint. This Stone Age portion of man's evolution spans about 90 per cent of his total time on earth as a human.

The Cro-Magnons apparently used paint freely on their bodies as well as in the caves

CRO-MAGNON MAN, A MODERN HUMAN BEING (CAUCASOID STOCK)

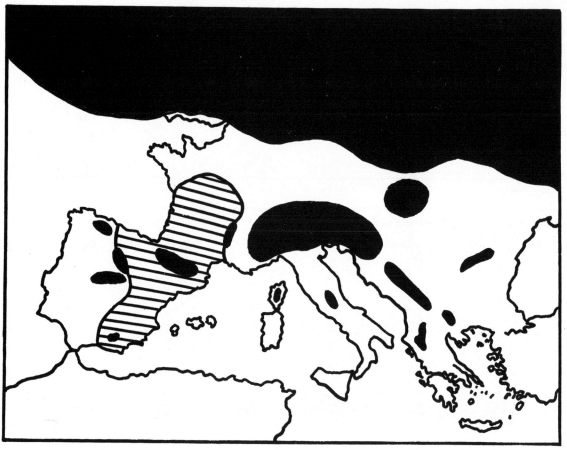

THE RANGE OF THE "CAVE MEN"

in which they conducted their rites. Some of their tools were beautiful and well finished; the people who followed them used essentially the same kind of tools but finished them more skillfully. Fishing, hunting of all sorts, the practice of medicine, the development of an art form, and the earliest attempts to band together large numbers of people for the common good mark the late ice age and the human beings who lived during that time.

Man Prepares To Settle Down

THE OLD Stone Age ended with Cro-Magnon man; the new Stone Age began even before the Cro-Magnons had fully disappeared. There is no sharp dividing line between the two ages, but basically it was the perfection of everything the people used, the exploitation of modes of transportation and hunting, and the growth of agricultural methods that made the real difference. The domestication of animals became an important part of human activity at this time. Taken together, all of these progressive trends very quickly led away from the Stone Age past and into the Bronze Age, Iron Age, and others that were to follow.

One of the last old Stone Age types that followed Cro-Magnon development was Chancelade man. This human being was a Northern European type with some Mongoloid features. In his relics there is evidence of increased skill in handling all of the materials known to man at that time.

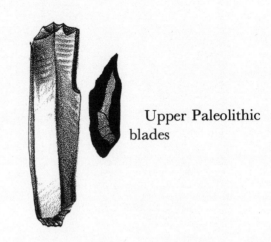

Upper Paleolithic blades

Mesolithic blades and drill

Neolithic tools and weapons

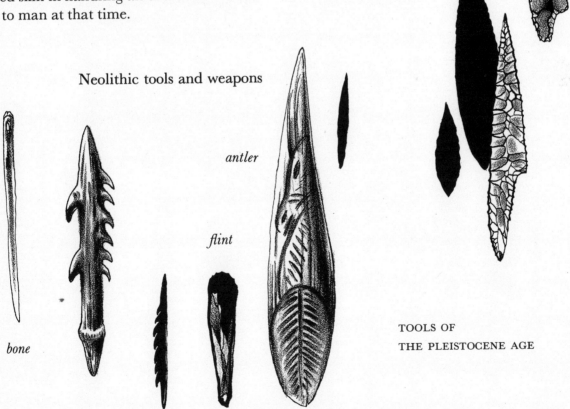

antler

flint

bone

TOOLS OF THE PLEISTOCENE AGE

91

CHANCELADE MAN, MIXED MONGOLOID AND CAUCASOID TYPES

It has been suggested that his total culture was probably very much like that of today's Eskimos, and it may have been even better in respect to craftsmanship in making clothing. At some time during this very late part of the ice age, the dog became part of the family group, not only as a hunting companion and pet but probably also as a dray animal for pulling loads. The wheel was invented toward the end of the old Stone Age.

The greatest cultures the world has known are supposed to have had their earliest beginnings at about this time; these were later centered around the Iranian Plateau and in what was called the Fertile Crescent, near the Mediterranean. Here the combination of hunting, agriculture, and animal husbandry blended to make possible man's broadest development. At the close of this time in history a large per cent of man's tools of the future had been invented. Large-scale farming and power beyond human strength were unknown, but they were just around the corner.

Long before man's cultural progress began to spread, what we call the races of modern man had begun to separate themselves, principally according to climate. People within tribal groupings began to want to live and work together or, in contrast, they sought isolation in a nomadic life of hunting.

Physically, human beings have not evolved significantly since the later part of the ice age, although their cultures and technology have undergone terrific changes that need no explanation here.

Significant in anthropology today are the continual discoveries of new, often fragmentary, specimens of ancient man made throughout the world that are extending our knowledge of the paths human evolution once took to achieve its present development. Two of these important specimens are the partial skulls from Kanjera and Kanam in Africa. The latter is a jaw. If the datings that have been tentatively assigned to these two specimens are correct, their implications are quite

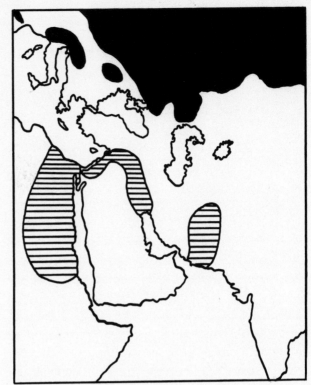

(*black = maximum extent of glacial ice*)

CENTERS OF CULTURAL GROWTH, 3000 B.C.

(All were adjacent to rich soil of
river valleys)

startling, for the Kanam jaw appears to date back 650,000 years before Christ. The skull from Kanjera dates back as early as 300,000 B.C.

All together, the facts about earliest men are even more astounding when we realize that what is described as a weak animal, the human being, was apparently much stronger and vigorously animallike hundreds of thousands of years ago, and that the basic animal stock from which human beings evolved must reach much farther back in history than present available fossil evidence permits us to realize. It is clearly possible that the prehuman animal line reaches back into the late Mesozoic Era when dinosaurs were still alive on earth.

The puzzle is to determine the unusual traits in human beings that encouraged the process of civilization among men.

93

Ice-age Art

MOST EVERYONE knows and has seen pictures of ice-age cave paintings, most of which are attributed to the Cro-Magnon race of human beings. Caverns in Spain and the southern central part of France have yielded the finest examples of this prehistoric art that the world knows, as well as many examples of incised bone, carvings in bone, some clay sculptures, finely made tools, collections of paint, and abundant evidence of elaborate religious and medical rites that were held within and near the caves. Some of this prehistoric cave painting compares favorably with the best in modern art. For the most part the animals represented are stylizations showing sufficient detail so that the most exacting paleontologists have found in them a verification of the animal reconstructions that were previously based on evidence taken from bones alone.

The Stone Age hunters who made these paintings obviously had close contact with their quarry. It stands to reason that the man who helped skin a freshly killed animal was very well equipped, if he had any art in his soul at all, to make a fine rendering of that animal. This was done time and time again. Some significance is attached to the fact that the animals shown in these paintings were animals that were hunted; it is thought that the omission of certain animals indicates that the creature was regarded as a totem, or favored animal, that was to be respected rather than killed.

One of the interesting factors of cave art is the representation of human beings dressed in the skins of animals. These were pictures of hunting significance or related to rites of initiation. Other stencil-type drawings on cave walls seem to have been made simply by holding a hand against the wall and blowing powdered pigment over it so that an outline was left. In this case, some of the hands that are printed show missing fingers.

Somewhat more crude than the cave paintings of Europe are the rock-shelter paintings found in Africa. Apparently these were made by natives of the Bushman type; the human beings represented in the outline drawings show many of the anatomical peculiarities of the Bushmen. Like the animals depicted in European caves, the African animals are accurately done and easily identifiable.

In the cave paintings there is a consistency of technique in the work that makes some students think that those men who showed talent along artistic lines were made responsible for creating practically all of this kind of work. Its uniform quality suggests that these men were job specialists, just as the men who had the most talent for chipping arrowheads or spear points were specialists.

Sculpture

Stencils from Castile

Wild ox from Teyjat

Line drawings

Bison

Bear and lioness
from Les Combarelles

Paintings from Altamira, Spain

Peccary

Horse, a bone carving

ICE-AGE ART

The Domestication of Animals

THE STORY of man and the other mammals has been linked inseparably since the ice age, and there have been many attempts to determine how man came to domesticate animals that are useful to him. Most theories agree that the dog was man's first triumph, for dogs were widely distributed, and their bones have been found with human remains in a way that suggests they were pets and camp followers. It is assumed that dogs were also useful hunting companions to the people of that time.

Some persons believe that pigs and sheep were penned and used as food at a very early time in man's civilization processes. These animals, being rather small, were fairly easy to control, and the pigs, in particular, were useful around village sites where they ate refuse, harmful insects, and reptiles. The process of domestication undoubtedly began by simply driving herds of smaller animals into a dead-end valley and then blocking the entrance. The animals could then be butchered for food when needed.

Wild cattle might have been the next kind of animal domesticated, and it is believed that this process took place in Northern Europe or in the Mediterranean area. Herds of hoofed mammals similar to modern cattle were so numerous in the ice age that they need not have feared man. The people of the times stayed close to these herds and finally came to realize that the temperament of certain species would permit them to feed and control them in corrals.

The primitive hunters who first discovered that the milk of cattle could be a readily controlled source of food stumbled upon one of the great keys to the success of evolution in all races of mankind. Without the cow's ability to create milk, none of the earth's populations could have spread and increased as they have. The spread of grasslands over the face of the earth also affected the distribution of man, for pasture land was vitally needed to sustain long migrations and the shiftings of large population groups. Successful migratory groups undoubtedly drove captive animals as a food source while they passed through unfamiliar lands.

Horses and men have been associated for many centuries, but many other animals may have been domesticated well before the horse was controlled. Cave-man art offers some clues to the animals that were most important in the lives of human beings during the Late Pleistocene Epoch. The horse is carved and painted frequently, but it was more than likely that he was a major food source long before his transport possibilities were utilized by man.

The domestication of most mammals was apparently a comparatively recent event. It was only a relatively few thousand years ago that man progressed from hunting to herding, farming, and breeding specialized food animals. Fossil records tell us little, but a few scattered discoveries indicate that animals were kept as a food supply in the dim past of civilization. One South American cave has shown the possible presence of crude pens in which ground sloths were kept to be butchered. If this theory is proven, this evidence is perhaps the earliest record of such animal use.

REINDEER

WILD OX

BISON

MAMMOTH

DOG—A
HUNTING
COMPANION
AS WELL

HORSE—LATER
ALSO USED FOR
TRANSPORTATION

WILD PIG

FOOD ANIMALS FOR ICE-AGE MAN

Dangerous Ice-age Mammals

THERE ARE still a few parts of the world where one of man's constant problems is the control of wild animals. Insects, reptiles, and other pesky small things have always been a nuisance, but they have not been the constant personal threat that flesh eaters of the ice age were to the people of that time. When human beings sought shelter in caves, there was always the danger of sharing that cave with a great bear, a lion, a saber-toothed cat, or any of several other wild beasts who used shallow rock shelters for hibernation or as a den during the birth of the young. It is supposed that where people had fire, the fire kept most of these animals at bay.

Hunting was also a period of great danger for the men. To date, no one has satisfactorily figured out how men of the ice age successfully killed mammoths and other animals of great size. It is popular to show Neanderthal or Cro-Magnon men at the edge of a huge pit into which such animals were apparently driven or lured. How such a pit could have been dug is unknown, and surely the animal within it would have fiercely attacked any human being who ventured near the edge of that kind of trap.

The modern rhinoceros has a vicious temperament which was undoubtedly just as bad in prehistoric times. This animal must have been one of the most dangerous to hunt; yet, judging from cave paintings and other indications that the rhinoceros was well known to these men, it was hunted. It is difficult to see how the members of such a hunting party could have escaped without severe damage to their number. Wolves, too, were among the most numerous of all ice-age animals, and they must have behaved exactly as their kind does today. Wherever wolf packs are numerous they are a severe threat to the safety of human beings.

Even the hoofed animals that are docile are sometimes very dangerous. It has been said repeatedly by sportsmen that if one added together all human deaths due to big mammals he would find that the ordinary farm bull would rank as the most dangerous big animal. Of course, any wounded animal will fight vigorously and in a deadly fashion.

It can be assumed that to avoid these personal dangers, the ice-age people banded together for their hunts. There is evidence in bone deposits that men, women, and even children combined their resources to form huge beating parties which surrounded herds of horses, cattle, or other animals. They then drove them over the edge of a cliff or into some other form of trap where the beasts with injuries could be killed with greater safety.

In any primitive economy, the women do a great deal of hunting; even today native women use a simple pointed stick to kill lizards, snakes, and other relatively harmless animals. It follows then that a stick in the hands of ice-age people—whether children or adults—was a major weapon. It could account for enough slow-moving game to make it possible for meat to have been a great part of the normal diet.

Ice-age hunters must have run terrible risks at times to kill their game or to fulfill some of the rites involved in initiating young boys into manhood. Even today, in primitive tribes where it is a distinction for a man to kill a dangerous beast single-handed, the bodies of the men are often horribly scarred and mutilated as a result of these encounters. To some natives it is a mark of great distinction to bear away the severed tail or mane of an animal that has been killed in fair hand-to-hand combat.

Such dangers in addition to all the other hardships of prehistoric peoples would have been an important factor in keeping down the human population in any given area.

SABER-TOOTHED CAT

DIRE WOLF

MAMMOTH

CAVE BEAR

WOOLLY RHINOCEROS

DANGEROUS ICE-AGE MAMMALS

Prehistoric Man in North America

WHEN COLUMBUS arrived in the New World he stepped backward in history many centuries; he found a Stone Age culture. The simplicity of the Indians' way of life left them open to conquest in any form—legal, military, moral, or cultural—and the utterly ruthless attitude of the white explorers toward the native Americans remains as one of the worst crimes committed against any racial group in all of history. The Indians who resisted longest were those best suited to nomadic hunting life. The slaughter of the buffalo broke their resistance and ability to survive independently of the white man's ways.

Nearly every anthropologist believes that the predecessors of North American and South American Indians came to the two continents by way of Asia, across the Bering Strait and down through Alaska and Canada. The routes these people took lay just east of the Rocky Mountains and in the broad area among the mountains just west of the Rockies. Precisely when these migrations took place is not known, but they did occur at a time when much of northeastern North America was still in the grip of glacial ice and probably while the water level in the Bering Strait was between 200 and 300 feet lower than it is now.

At least three crossing methods were possible. If the water was as low as some people believe it was, a dry-land crossing could have taken place. There is also a possibility that the migrants came from Asia at a time when ice bridged the gap between land masses or that they made a boat crossing. Although there is no specific evidence to support this latter notion, it is known that ice-age man did make and use boats.

All of the pre-Columbian inhabitants of the New World show a strong relationship to Mongoloid peoples. Northern Eskimos, Mexican Indians, South American racial groups, and the North American Indians all fall into one of the numerous subdivisions of the basic Mongoloid stock of Asia.

These earliest immigrants into North America were a nomadic and hardy people. For many centuries their fate on this continent was very closely tied to the herds of game animals. Nearly all of the important evidence of North American primitive men is derived from sites where accumulated animal bones are the dominant feature. The first acceptable relics of ice-age men in North America were found in 1929 at Folsom, New

Clovis type

Folsom type

Sandia type

IMPORTANT TYPICAL POINTS MADE
BY EARLY AMERICAN MAN

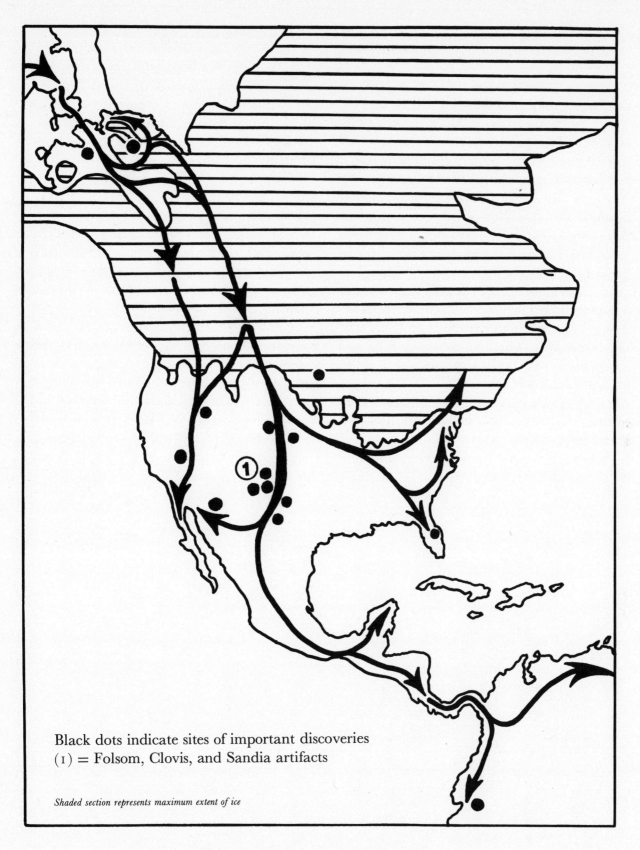

Black dots indicate sites of important discoveries
(1) = Folsom, Clovis, and Sandia artifacts

Shaded section represents maximum extent of ice

MIGRATION ROUTES INTO NORTH AMERICA

México. Distinctive spear points were found there in direct association with the remains of extinct bison.

So many North American finds of artifacts were made on the surface of the earth that for many years their potential value was discounted. The bones of extinct mammals of the ice age have provided the most positive indication of the antiquity of man in North America. Mastodons, mammoths, unusual bison, sloths, and other animals not found on this continent when the first explorers arrived were well represented in the camp litter of prehistoric people.

Archaeologists in the southwestern United States had to move with caution whenever new finds were made, because the layers of silt and dust that had covered most sites was easily disturbed. Soil cover was measured in fractions of an inch instead of in feet, and special techniques of plotting the finds were required to insure accuracy in dating the materials.

Almost no skeletal remains are available to help round out our picture of prehistoric North Americans. Those skulls and other fragments that are known have come principally from the Southwest. One important discovery was made in Florida and another in Minnesota. None of these bones indicate anatomical features different from those of Indians that were here when the white man first invaded the continent.

Unique weapon points and a few ornaments are virtually the only clues we have to the human beings who lived in North America at least 23,800 years ago. The people of that time used fire, but their roving habits contributed to the scarcity of their remains. Severe weather has erased nearly all of the evidence that they ever lived.

Coming closer to the present, we find that about 10,000 years ago primitive Americans were making baskets and clothing and were building crude houses. There are more discoveries relative to these civilizations principally because some of the people had begun to live in caves and to stay in one area for longer periods of time. Agriculture had become a factor in the lives of the people.

Prehistoric Man in South America

THE PREHISTORY of South American Indian types is less known than that of any other continent. Actual human remains of any importance have been found in only three countries: Ecuador, Chile, and Brazil. The intense desire of many South American countries to establish good museums will eventually lead to wider knowledge of the earliest human beings on that continent, but lush tropical vegetation hides much valuable material that will never be seen. Some anthropologists are particularly eager to show that the oldest native people may have come from the South Pacific area on rafts of great size.

When anthropology was a struggling science, one patriotic South American made a bold attempt to establish the origin of man on that continent. The evidence presented was a mixture of recent and old bones that were later proven to have been incorrectly identified. At another time, a poor photographic print of a supposedly prehuman primate was offered as evidence of the prehistory of man in South America. Nothing in the picture gave a clue to the true size of the animal. This photo turned out to be nothing more than a picture of an oversize spider monkey whose tail had been cut off or hidden behind the log on which the animal was posed.

The primitive people living at the extreme southern tip of South America exist in a harsh, wet, cold climate and display no evidence of cultural progress. These Fuegean people did not normally use clothing, and the only shelter for the family was a wind screen made from skins supported by a few sticks. When efforts were made to civilize them, the colonists offered them clothing which absorbed the water in the seacoast air, and the resulting chills brought sickness and death to many families. Further efforts to help them live in better houses led to more illness and virtual extinction of the people of Tierra del Fuego. In both North and South America the native peoples and their cultures could not successfully adapt to the vigor of the cultures brought by Europeans.

FOLSOM MAN

The Basic Racial Stocks of Recent Man

WHEN Christopher Columbus discovered America in 1492, there were at least six major racial groups of human beings alive in our world. These groups were the big three—Negroid, Caucasoid, and Mongoloid—and the Bushmen, the Australians, and the basic Pacific type of human being that was a mixture of light and dark-skinned people.

At that time the racial stock with the widest distribution was the Mongoloid. These people spread over most of Asia, the lands of the South Pacific, and all of North and South America. Some people believe that the successful existence of any animal depends on the wide distribution of the basic stock. Some parts of the Mongoloid range were thinly populated, but if this theory follows in human animals, then it could be assumed that Mongoloids might have been the original stock from which all men developed.

In 1492, Caucasoid stocks were the next most widely distributed type of people, and the third largest group was the Negroid. As you might expect, most of the darker-skinned peoples of the world were generally to be found in lands that lie on the equator or very near it. Throughout all of the ranges of man each system or division between the races is found to blend and mix with its neighbor.

PRIMITIVE HUNTERS OF THE WORLD

The six racial stocks of man mentioned above are more mixed and interbred today, but in remote parts of the world there are still a few primitive hunting people. In our own country the Californian and Basin Indian tribes are considered such. In South America the Patagonians and other people living near Tierra del Fuego are primitive hunters. In Africa it is the Bushmen who are the most primitive, and there are primitive hunters in Australia and Tasmania. The people of the Andaman Islands in the Bay of Bengal between India and Burma are also primitive hunters.

Each of these isolated people are quite distinct from the other races that live near-by and in most cases they are very hard to classify. In general, their size, facial appearance, and many of their cultural traits imply great mixing of people and long isolation from contact with more vigorous races. They usually live in lands that are quite barren and inhospitable; many of them dwell in desert country. They live off the land and hunt vigorously, leaving little game as a carry-over breeding stock which they may hunt again in the future. They are apt to do very little food preparation, and much of their food is eaten raw. Some Eskimo types could be included in this list of primitive hunters, but the Eskimos have been so influenced by sailors and traders that they are rapidly losing or have already lost their dependence on simple Stone Age methods of hunting.

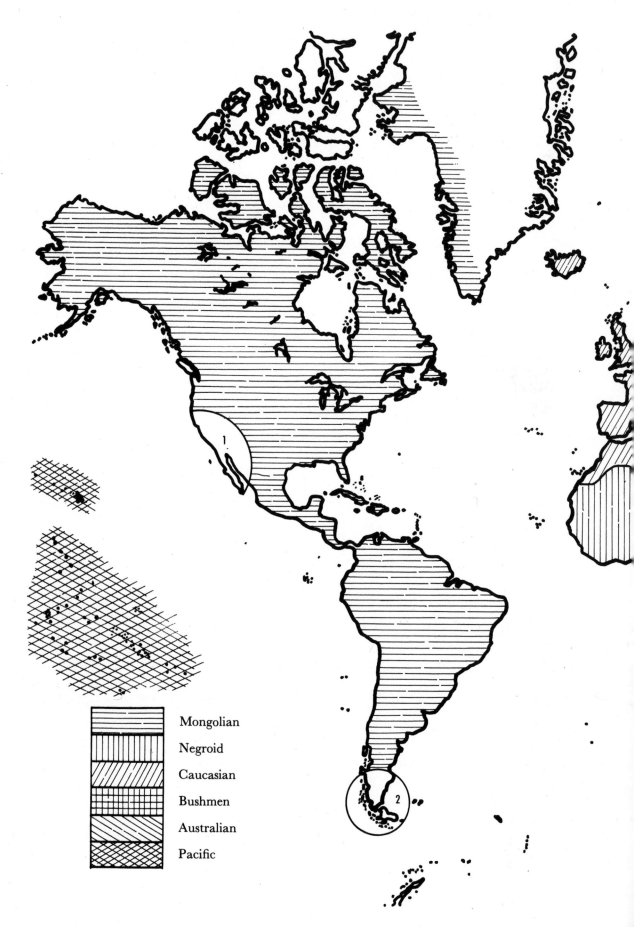

Mongolian

Negroid

Caucasian

Bushmen

Australian

Pacific

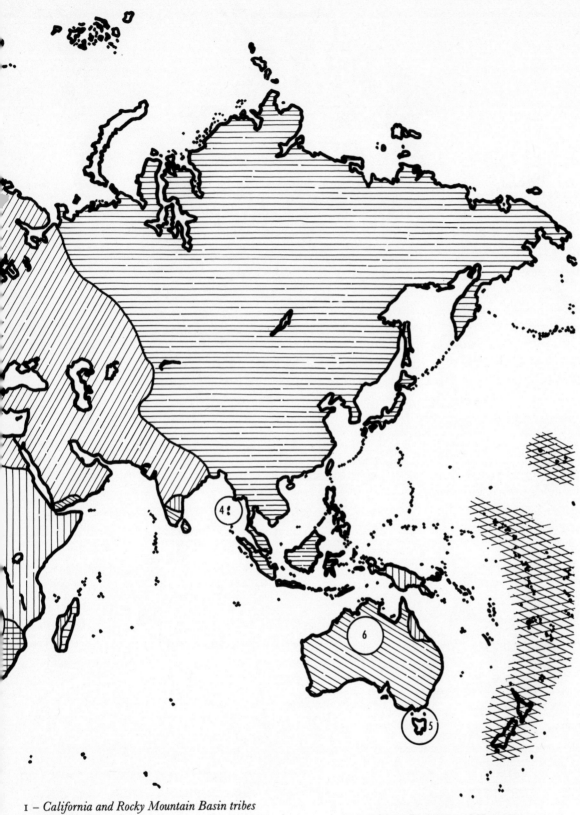

1 – *California and Rocky Mountain Basin tribes*
2 – *Fuegians*
    Patagonians
    Onas
    Yaghans

3 – *African Bushmen and Hottentots*
4 – *Andaman Islanders*
5 – *Tasmanians*
6 – *Australian aborigines*

SIX BASIC RACIAL STOCKS

Modern Races of Mankind

TODAY'S ANTHROPOLOGIST has at his disposal so many ways of classifying human beings that it is difficult to list them all, and yet it should be clearly understood that external physical characteristics are by no means the only factors used by science to compare races. These outward characteristics are enough, however, to break the primary stocks into at least twenty or more racial types that are readily identifiable in the world to-day.

In the past, measurements of the human head, a tabulation of skin color, height, weight, and the like were all that people had to work with in solving or stating questions of race. Today, such complex things as the structure of the blood, the chemistry of the body in general, the careful comparison of unborn hu-

man embryos with those of other animals, and many more detailed determining factors are available for study.

In describing a race, the adult male is used as the standard for comparison.

If delineation of races into minute categories is required, skin color is one of the primary determining factors of race. The chemistry and the growth of skin is now quite well understood. Hair form and hair color are factors; so are eye structure and eye color and the association of hair and eye color. The form of the human head; the form of the face; the shape, size, and placement of the nose; the shape and size of the ears; lips; finger and palm and footprints; the location and functioning of glands; and total height—all these are just a few of the points that are studied to determine race.

There are also many basic physiologic tests that are made to help determine race. These include temperature, pulse, and metabolism rates, the rate of growth of young children, such things as color blindness, the response to medicines, and even the response to weather and dietary changes. To the average person all of these things may seem too much trouble to take merely to sort people, but judging from the arguments that continually revolve around the definition of race, these are indeed not too great a subdivision of characteristics to be considered.

It is a mistake to believe that there is no structural difference between the blood of different races, that skin color is unimportant, or that any similar factors are not important. The use of loose statements to the contrary by international good-will groups may be jus-

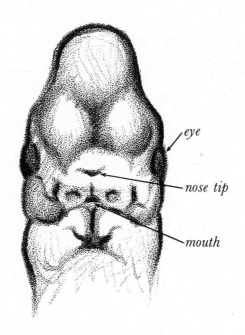

eye

nose tip

mouth

THE HUMAN FACE AS SEEN
IN A 7-WEEKS-OLD FETUS

tifiable and will probably continue; indeed, their use may help people smooth over the differences among themselves and eventually create a greater respect for all the people of the world and a better co-operation between religious and nationality groups now separated by artificial boundaries that create great tensions. Actually most of what we have come to call racial discrimination is not based upon a difference between races; it is really based on what we have allowed ourselves to consider as undesirable to us socially.

A race is a relatively small division of the basic human stock into the subspecies level. In nature, an animal subspecies is seldom of any great importance in understanding large concepts; biologically, subspecies are only

Medium build, any height

Wavy or straight hair of any color but a dull black

Eyes can be almost any shade except black

White to light-brown skin

BASIC CAUCASOID

Woolly or frizzy black hair

Dark eyes

Brown to blue-black skin Medium to thin muscular build, any height

BASIC NEGROID

slight variations of a basic form, and so it is with *Homo sapiens*.

Very few anthropologists can agree just how many races warrant separation. The listing of races on the following pages is in part based on that favored by the late Earnest A. Hooton. Only major racial types are illustrated; those people exhibiting extreme mix-

tures of features are simply listed by their common racial names.

In order to distinguish races, scientists have adopted a pattern of descriptive phrases that account for a very fine degree of variation be-

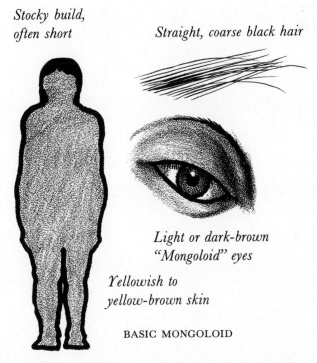

Stocky build, often short

Straight, coarse black hair

Light or dark-brown "Mongoloid" eyes

Yellowish to yellow-brown skin

BASIC MONGOLOID

109

tween human beings. These are listed below in the order of their importance and briefly explained.

A. *Sorting criteria*—methods and features uniformly tabulated after study of very large numbers of individuals.

B. *Characters*—these are general terms for description used when the people described are so genetically mixed that normal sorting features cannot be applied.

1. *Primary racial stocks*—Caucasoid, or White; Negroid; Mongoloid.

2. *Primary subraces*—includes the most obvious subgroups of the primary stocks.

3. *Morphological types*—smaller, localized subgroups that can often be identified visually but do not sort readily by measurements due to the subtle blending of their features.

4. *Composite primary subraces*

5. *Residual mixed types*

6. *Composite races*

These are too detailed for practical use by any but the most advanced students of anthropology.

Primary Stock—

Caucasoid, or White

Sorting criteria—Skin color varies from white to light brown. Hair color is seldom black but can be any lighter shade. The form of the hair is never woolly but can be anything else. Eyes are never black but are all other lighter shades.

Characters—Facial and body hair is anything from medium to very abundant. There is usually no projection of the face. The lips are medium to thin. The chin is a prominent facial feature. The texture of the hair is seldom coarse; it is usually fine. The nose is usually high and narrow, but it is never flat at the base. The pelvic area in both sexes is broad.

PRIMARY SUBRACES
  Classic Mediterranean
    Morphological Types
    Atlanto Mediterranean
    Iranian Plateau
  Alpine
  Armenoid
  Nordic
  Keltic
  Eastern Baltic
  Ainu
COMPOSITE SUBRACES
  Armenoid
  Dinaric
    Morphological Types
    Beaker

RESIDUAL MIXED TYPES
  Nordic-Alpine
  Nordic-Mediterranean
COMPOSITE RACES—BASICALLY WHITE
  Australian
    Morphological Types
    Murrian
    Carpentarian
    Tasmanoid
COMPOSITE RACES—BASICALLY NEGROID
  Tasmanian
  Classic Indo-Dravidian
    Morphological Types
    Armenoid-Iranian Plateau
    Indo-Nordic
    Australoid (Veddoid)
    Negritoid
  Polynesian

The primary white race is considered to have produced the earliest form of erect thinking man. Because the white stock is considered very old, it has been broken down into many more subraces and growth types than are seen in the Negroids and Mongoloids. It should be remembered that anthropologists have studied the white race more than any other racial type, and that more exploratory digging has been done in countries that would be expected to produce skeletons of white races.

Mediterranean—long-headed brunet
Range: Mediterranean Basin, other parts of Europe, and the Near East

Armenoid—brunet, hook-nosed, long head, mixture of Mediterranean, Alpine, and Iranian Plateau types
Range: Turkey, Syria, Palestine, Iran, Iraq

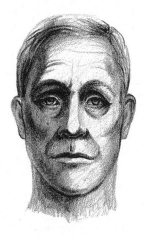

Nordic—blond, long head
Range: Scandinavia, Baltic areas, United States, British colonies, thinly spread through Europe

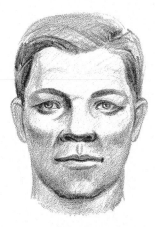

Alpine—broad-nosed, brunet, round head
Range: Central Europe

Keltic—light eyes, dark or red-headed, long head, usually considered a modern replica of the Cro-Magnon man
Range: Northern and western British Isles, thinly spread through Europe

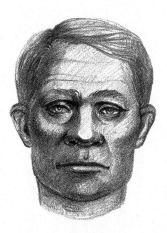

Eastern Baltic—blond, round head, broad-nosed
Range: Northern Europe, well into Russia

Drawings by Joann S. Scheele

Ainu—hairy, long-headed brunet
Range: Northern Japan, Sakhalin Island

Australian—archaic man, mixture of Archaic White, Tasmanian, minor Melanesian, and Papuan
Range: Wastelands of Australia

Tasmanian—Negrito and Australian bloods
Range: now extinct as a racial type, but blood traces are still strong in the Pacific area

Indo-Dravidian—basically White, but carries blood of Mediterranean, Australoid, Negrito, and minor parts of many other types
Range: lower classes throughout India, is nearly a classic Mediterranean type

Dinaric—light-skinned, hooked-nosed, round head, carries blood of extinct Whites, Alpine, Nordic, and Armenoid types
Range: Yugoslavia, Austrian Tyrol, and Central Europe

Berber—basically White, nearly blond, a living Stone Age racial and cultural people
Range: North Africa

Polynesian—brunet, White, carries blood of White, Indonesian, Mongoloid, Melanesian, and Papuan types
Range: fringe islands of the Pacific, Hawaii

Drawings by Joann S. Scheele

Primary Stock—
Negroid

Sorting criteria—The hair form is woolly or frizzy and the color of the hair is always black. The skin color is dark brown to black. The eye color is dark brown to black, and the average nasal index is very broad.

Characters—The projection of the face below the nose is usually considerable. The nose is broad and in profile usually appears to be concave. The tip of the nose is usually elevated; the nostrils are thick and flare widely. Lips are thick and their surfaces turn outward. The form of the face is short, and the cheek bones are prominent. The chin is usually round and does not project as it does in white races. Most head forms are long. Hair on the head is short, and the facial and body hair is thin. Ears are generally small and fit close to the head. Lower arms and legs are quite long in proportion to the rest of each limb. The calf of the leg is usually quite small, and the heel projects prominently. The pelvis in both male and female is narrow.

PRIMARY SUBRACES
Forest Negro
Nilotic Negro
Negrito
    Morphological Types
Infantile
Adultiform

COMPOSITE RACES
Oceanic Negroid
    Secondary Subraces
Papuan
Melanesian
Bushman-Hottentot
    Secondary Subraces
Bushman
Hottentot

1. Berbers
2. African Whites
3. Zone of mixtures
4. Nilotic Negro
5. Somali types
6. Forest Negro
7. Pygmy
8. Bantu types
9. Bushmen
10. Hottentots

THE RACIAL TYPES OF AFRICA

Nilotic Negro—small amount of Mediterranean blood
Range: upper waters of the White and Blue Nile

Negrito
    Range: Congo forest, Andaman Islands, Malay Peninsula, Philippines, and New Guinea

Forest Negro
Range: forested Africa near the equator and adjacent areas

Bushman-Hottentot—carries blood of Negrito, extinct Boskop, and minor parts of Forest Negro and Mediterranean types
Range: desert, Southwest Africa

Oceanic Negroid—carries blood of Negrito, Australoid, Mediterranean, and minor parts of Malay and Polynesian types
Range: Pacific islands

Primary Stock—

Mongoloid

Sorting criteria—Hair is black, straight, and of a coarse texture. Skin color is yellow to yellow brown. Eyes are medium to dark brown. The eye form is slitlike, heavy-lidded, slanted and gives the appearance of being close to the surface of the face. Cheek bones are strongly projected front and sideways, and they are usually covered with a thick layer of fat. The quantity of hair on the face and body is less than that of any other racial group. The nose is of middle breadth. The tip is short when seen in profile. The nose is straight or more often concave; it is considered to have an infantile appearance.

Characters—The body build usually shows broad, muscular shoulders, a long trunk, and short legs. The calf of the leg is very muscular. As a group the Mongoloids are short. Their teeth often project forward from the mouth, and the incisors are peculiarly shovel-shaped. In young children there is a dark spot in the sacral region that is called the Mongoloid spot; it disappears with maturity.

PRIMARY SUBRACES
  Classic Mongoloid
  Arctic Mongoloid (Eskimoid)
COMPOSITE RACES
  Indonesian-Malay
  Secondary Subraces
  Malay-Mongoloid
  Indonesian
  American Indian
  Morphological Types
  Broad Heads
    Hawk-nosed Types common in North America
    Snub-nosed Types generally in central South America
  Long Heads
    Hawk-nosed Types—occurs generally
    Snub-nosed Types—occurs generally

The foregoing division of the basic human stocks into racial subgroupings includes more varieties of human beings than the average class in anthropology needs to study, but they are by no means all it is possible to describe.

One of the problems of anthropology as a

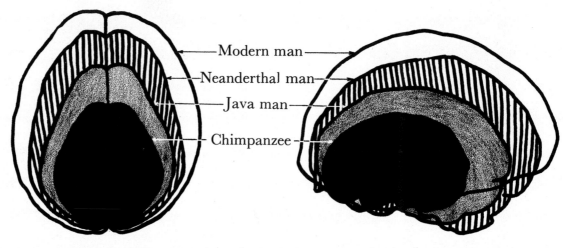

COMPARATIVE BRAIN SIZES

Indonesian-Malay—carries blood of Mongoloid, Ainu, Negrito, and Mediterranean types
Range: south China, Burma, Indo-China, Siam, and Malay Archipelago

Arctic Mongoloid (Eskimoid)
Range: Arctic North America, northeastern Asia

Classic Mongoloid
Range: Siberia, north China, Mongolia, and Tibet

South American Indian—round head, snub-nosed or long head, hawk-nosed
Range: South America

North American Indian—hawk-nosed, broad head, carries blood of Mongoloid, Iranian Plateau, Australoid, and minor parts of Negrito types; also snub-nosed
Range: Canada and United States

Drawings by Joann S. Scheele

117

science is to show the interrelation of human beings and thus illustrate just how false most of our notions about race are. It is difficult, for instance, to find any way of evaluating the relative *degree* of evolution in any great racial group. Science has never made any serious attempt to state that any one race is superior or inferior to another. It should also be said that science has likewise never stated that all races are equal either in their cultural development or in their biological development. The basic problem of helping races to understand each other, to think about their problems and the factors that are working upon them, still remains. No matter what scientists may discover to help pacify human beings on the subject of human origins, it still remains the job of the teachers of the world to guide people's thinking away from those who wish to exploit differences of physical structure or cultural development that separate the peoples of the world into races.

Race has never limited anyone's ability to think.

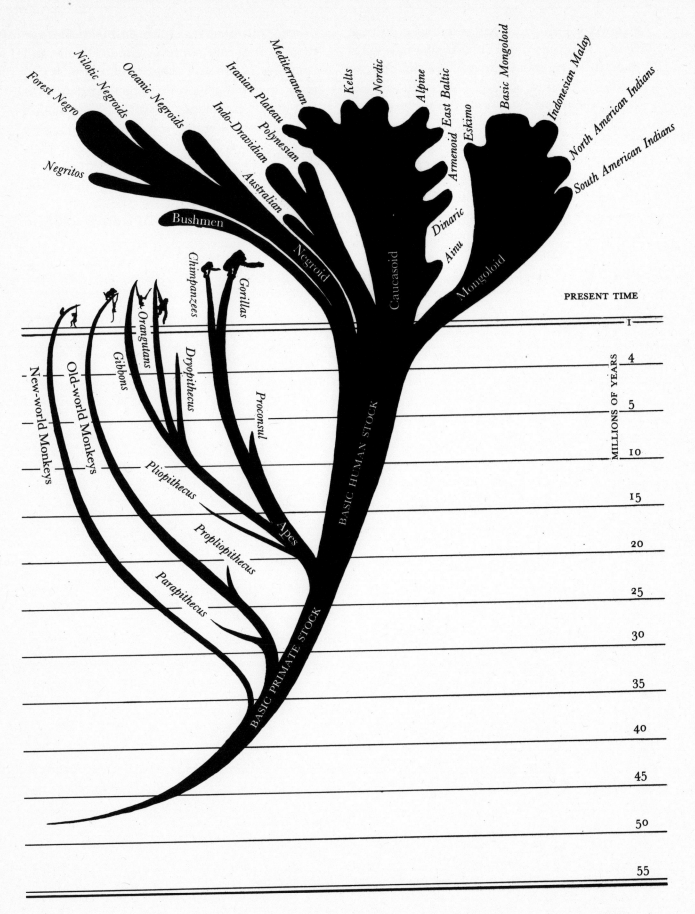

Forest Negro

Nilotic Negroids

Oceanic Negroids

Negritos

Iranian Plateau

Indo-Dravidian

Mediterranean

Polynesian

Australian

Kelts

Nordic

Alpine

East Baltic

Armenoid

Eskimo

Basic Mongoloid

Indonesian Malay

North American Indians

South American Indians

Bushmen

Chimpanzees

Gorillas

Orangutans

Dryopithecus

Gibbons

Procorsul

Negroid

Caucasoid

Dinaric

Ainu

Mongoloid

New-world Monkeys

Old-world Monkeys

Pliopithecus

Apes

Propliopithecus

Parapithecus

BASIC HUMAN STOCK

BASIC PRIMATE STOCK

PRESENT TIME

MILLIONS OF YEARS

1

4

5

10

15

20

25

30

35

40

45

50

55

CHART OF THE RACES OF MAN AND THE HIGHER PRIMATES

BIBLIOGRAPHY

CARRINGTON, RICHARD. *The Story of Our Earth.* New York: Harper and Brothers, Publishers, 1956.

CLARK, W. E. LE GROS. *The Fossil Evidence for Human Evolution.* Chicago: The University of Chicago Press, 1955.

COLBERT, EDWIN H. *Evolution of the Vertebrates.* New York: John Wiley and Sons, Inc., 1955.

COON, CARLETON S. *The Story of Man.* New York: Alfred A. Knopf, Inc., 1954.

DUNLOP, JAMES M. *Anatomical Diagrams.* New York: The Macmillan Co., 1949.

FLINT, RICHARD FOSTER. *Glacial Geology and the Pleistocene Epoch.* New York: John Wiley and Sons, Inc., 1947.

HAWKES, JACQUETTA. *Man on Earth.* New York: Random House, 1955.

HERSKOVITS, MELVILLE J. *Cultural Anthropology.* New York: Alfred A. Knopf, Inc., 1955.

HILL, W. C. OSMAN. *Primates.* New York: Interscience Publishers, Inc., 1953–56.

HOFFMAN, MALVINA. *Heads and Tales.* New York: Garden City Publishing Co., Inc., 1943.

HOGBEN, LANCELOT. *From Cave Painting to Comic Strip.* New York: Chanticleer Press, Inc., 1949.

HOOTON, EARNEST ALBERT. *Up From the Ape,* rev. ed. New York: The Macmillan Co., 1947.

HOWELLS, WILLIAM. *Mankind So Far.* New York: Doubleday and Co., Inc., 1944.

KROEBER, A. L. *Anthropology,* rev. ed. New York: Harcourt, Brace and Co., 1948.

LINTON, RALPH. *The Tree of Culture.* New York: Alfred A. Knopf, Inc., 1955.

MOORE, RUTH. *Man, Time, and Fossils.* New York: Alfred A. Knopf, Inc., 1953.

OSBORN, HENRY FAIRFIELD. *Men of the Old Stone Age.* New York: Charles Scribner's Sons, 1915.

ROMER, ALFRED S. *Man and the Vertebrates,* 3rd ed. Chicago: The University of Chicago Press, 1941.

———. *The Vertebrate Body,* 2nd ed. Philadelphia: W. B. Saunders Co., 1955.

SANDERSON, IVAN T. *Living Mammals of the World.* New York: Garden City Books, 1955.

TITIEV, MISCHA. *The Science of Man.* New York: Henry Holt and Co., Inc., 1954.

WEIDENREICH, FRANZ. *Anthropological Papers.* New York: The Viking Fund, 1949.

———. *Apes, Giants, and Man.* Chicago: The University of Chicago Press, 1946.

YOUNG, J. Z. *The Life of the Vertebrates.* New York: Oxford University Press, Inc., 1950.

Many magazine articles were source material; most were from:
Life magazine, published by Time, Inc.
National Geographic magazine, published by the National Geographic Society
Natural History magazine, published by the American Museum of Natural History
Scientific American magazine, published by Scientific American, Inc.

About the Author

WILLIAM E. SCHEELE, Curator of the Cleveland Museum of Natural History, was born in Cleveland in 1920. He won scholarships in art and biology and was graduated from Western Reserve University in 1947. In November, 1939, he won the first annual Bird Art Contest, sponsored by the Cleveland Museum of Natural History, and the next day he was a member of their staff. In 1949, after army service had interrupted his career, he was appointed director of the museum; he is one of the youngest museum directors in the country. Mr. Scheele's outside activities include painting natural-history subjects (he has exhibited in many museums), gem cutting, and fossil hunting. All of his non-working hours are spent with his wife and three sons on their tree farm near Chardon, Ohio.

This book was set on the Fotosetter in
Baskerville and Bulmer types by
Westcott and Thomson, Inc.
It was printed by
Copifyer Lithograph Corporation on
Perkins and Squier Company's
RR Wove
made by P. H. Glatfelter Company.
The binding was done at
The Press of The World Publishing Company.
Typography and design are by
Ernst Reichl Associates

1 2 3 4 5 6 7 8 9 10 66 65 64 63 62 61 60 59 58 57